Official
National Test Practice Papers

Key Stage 3
Age 13-14

KEY STAGE 3
MATHS TESTS

London: The Stationery Office

Test material text © Qualifications and Curriculum Authority 1998

Introduction p. v © The Stationery Office 1998

Text material p. ix–x © The Times 1998

ISBN 0 11 370056 3

Key Stage Tests

Mathematics, Key Stage 3, Age 13–14

Contents

Introduction

This one of three books which will help you work with your child to prepare for the tests almost all children take in Year 9 at the end of Key Stage 3 at about age 14. Using them will also give you some information about what your child knows in English, mathematics and science – known as the core subjects of the National Curriculum.

This book helps you and your child practise the mathematics tests. The other two books help practise the English tests and the science tests.

There are a number of books in the shops which set out to do this for Key Stages 1 and 2, but these are the only ones for Key Stage 3.

The three books contain last year's tests which were taken by 14 year olds. Using them gives your child a chance to get used to the tests and how to take them. They will also tell you more about how your child is doing in three key subjects. So they are one of the best ways you can help your child make progress.

The tests and how they help your child

Finding out what children know and can do is an important part of their education. It:

- helps teachers produce better plans and better classroom teaching
- helps children think about their own learning
- gives you information about your child
- helps you help your child at home
- builds up a picture of how well schools are doing.

This information is gained in three main ways.

1. Day by day, month by month, term by term, your child's teachers build up a picture of your child through the work they mark and through watching your child at work in the classroom.

   When you get your child's report each year and see your child's teacher in school at an open evening, you will receive a summary of this information.

2. At the ages of 7, 11 and 14 your child's work is assessed more formally. Your child's teachers will use the records they have made and make judgements about how your child is doing against the National Curriculum; this is called Teacher Assessment.

3. At the same time your child will also take the national tests in English, Mathematics and science – except for the 7 year olds, who do not have a science test. Almost every child in the country in those age groups take the same tests. Although they do not test everything, they cover some of the most important work your child has done in school in each of the three subjects.

When the tests have been marked, your child will be awarded a 'Level' in each subject, based on how they performed in the tests. Both the Teacher Assessment levels and the test levels have to be given to you as part of the school's report.

How to use this book

What is being tested?

This book contains last year's tests in mathematics for 14 year olds. These tests are based on the National Curriculum so you need to know a little about how it's organised.

The National Curriculum for mathematics is divided into five sections (or Attainment Targets):

1. Using and Applying Mathematics

2. Number

3. Algebra

4. Shape, Space and Measures

5. Handling Data

The tests

In 1997 the mathematics tests consisted of two papers, Paper 1 and Paper 2, at four Tiers. Each paper took 1 hour.

Every child takes Paper 1 and Paper 2, at one of four Tiers, Tier 3–5, 4–6, 5–7 or Tier 6–8, depending on their level of attainment. Particularly able pupils can also take an Extension Paper. In Paper 1 in each of the four Tiers your child will not be allowed to use a calculator, but they can do so in Paper 2.

A number of questions in the two papers are duplicated in each Tier (which overlap in Levels). Additionally, it is not possible for parents to know beforehand their child's level of attainment and so practise the correct Tier tests. For these reasons, therefore, the questions included in this book are not graded into the four 'Tiers', but are included in order of increasing difficulty, extending from attainment Level 3 to Level 8. This enables you to work with your child to practise the tests to a level at which they are comfortable. Don't expect your child to answer all the questions. The Extension Paper is not included.

In 1998 there will be a mental arithmetic test for pupils working at Level 3 or above. The marks from the mental arithmetic test will be added to the marks from Papers 1 and 2 to give an overall subject award at Levels 3 to 8. The mental arithmetic test will have a weighting of 20 per cent. Each mental arithmetic test will be a 20 minute taped test consisting of 30 questions.

How you can help your child prepare for the mathematics tests

- Be encouraging and supportive, so that your child is confident about the tests.

- Talk with your child's teacher about how you can help your child improve, so that you can support and build on the work done in class.

- Be interested in your child's work and talk about it. Try not to nag or be critical.

- Try to take advantage of opportunities to get your child to do mental arithmetic or to use mathematics in practical everyday situations, such as shopping, comparing and estimating prices, weighing and measuring things, looking at graphs, diagrams, charts, etc, in books, newspapers and magazines and saying what they mean.

- Don't let your own worries about tests – if you have any – pass on to your child.

Hints for your child on taking the tests

1. Listen carefully to the teacher's instructions for the tests and follow them exactly.

2. Read the questions carefully.

3. If you're not sure, ask for help. The teacher can't tell you the answers but will be able to help you understand what it is you have to do.

4. Don't be afraid to make a sensible guess if you are not entirely sure of the answer.

5. Don't worry if you can't answer all the questions, leave out the ones you can't do and make sure you do answer all the ones you can.

6. If you get stuck on a question, move on to the next one and come back to it later.

7. If there's time after you've tried all the questions, check the answers very carefully.

Preparing for the tests

by John O'Leary, Education Editor of *The Times*.

Tests at the end of Key Stage 3 give parents and pupils their last chance to gauge progress before the onset of GCSE. They can be an invaluable guide to areas of strength and weakness, as well as providing an opportunity to polish up that all-important exam technique.

Although the results will not be used for league tables, they do give parents a check on a school's standards at a stage of education which inspectors have often found weak. Schools are obliged not only to publish national curriculum test results, but to set them in a national context.

As the last national tests before GCSE, the Key Stage 3 tests give 14-year-olds the chance to try out their revision skills in an arena which will not affect their long-term prospects. This book allows them to focus their work on the right areas and to plan for the type of questions they will face in the spring.

Assessment now takes place in all national curriculum subjects, but formal tests are limited to the core subjects of English, maths and science. The sample questions in this book are all taken from last year's tests, which will be similar this time.

Schools will run their own revision classes, but a little extra familiarisation, using the test examples, will aid this process. It will also show parents, for whom the tests will be unchartered territory, some of the concepts their children should have mastered by the age of 14.

There is no right or wrong way to prepare for these or any other tests. What suits one child may be quite wrong for another. But there are some basic points that hold good for most examinees, whatever the subject.

Thinking ahead

Perhaps the most important rule, whatever the subject, is not to leave revision to the last moment. Decide what you need to go over several weeks before the test, discuss it with your teacher and set aside some time. Find out what the school's revision plans are, and make sure that yours do not clash.

Do not revise in front of the television. A short period of concentrated work is worth hours shared with *Neighbours* or *Top of the Pops*. Find somewhere quiet, if possible, and do not allow yourself to be distracted.

Use the test examples to get an idea of what will be required in the test, but do not assume that your questions will be in the same areas. Make sure you are confident about all the main topics that you have covered.

In the week of the test

Divide your time between the different subjects, concentrating on weaknesses. Use the practice questions in this book, but do not overdo last-minute revision: you want to be alert for the test itself.

On the day

Make sure you have any materials needed for the test and that you are on time. Then try to relax. In the end, the tests are just another step on the way to GCSE.

Combined Paper 1 Questions, Levels 3–8

Write your name and school in the spaces below.

First Name _____

Last Name _____

School _____

Remember

- Answer as many questions as you can in 1 hour. You are *not* expected to answer all the questions.

- You **must not** use a calculator for any question in this test.

- You will need: pen, pencil, rubber, ruler, tracing paper and mirror (optional).

- Some formulae you might need are on page 3.

- This test starts with easier questions.

- Write all your answers and working on the test paper - do not use any rough paper.

- Check your work carefully.

- Ask if you are not sure what to do.

Instructions

Formulae

You might need to use these formulae.

AREA

Rectangle

length × width

Circle

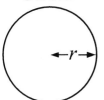

πr^2

Take π as 3.14

Triangle

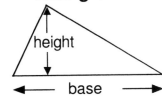

$\dfrac{\text{base} \times \text{height}}{2}$

Parallelogram

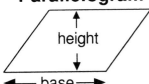

base × height

Trapezium

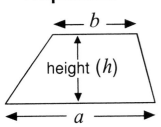

$\dfrac{(a + b)}{2} \times h$

LENGTH

Circle

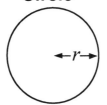

circumference $= 2\pi r$

For a right-angled triangle

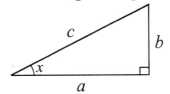

$a^2 + b^2 = c^2$ (Pythagoras' theorem)

$a = c \cos x$ $\qquad \cos x = \dfrac{a}{c}$

$b = c \sin x$ $\qquad \sin x = \dfrac{b}{c}$

$b = a \tan x$ $\qquad \tan x = \dfrac{b}{a}$

VOLUME

Prism

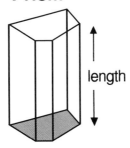

area of cross-section × length

1.

(a)   A shop sells square carpet tiles.
The edge of a carpet tile is $\frac{1}{2}$m long.

6 carpet tiles can fit together on a floor like this:

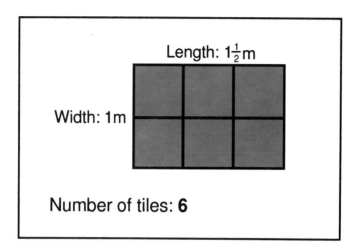

Length: $1\frac{1}{2}$m

Width: 1m

Number of tiles: **6**

Write how many carpet tiles fit on each of the two floors shown below.
You can draw the tiles if you want to.

Length: 2m

Width:
1m

Number of tiles: ....

Length: $1\frac{1}{2}$m

Width:
$1\frac{1}{2}$m

Number of tiles: ....

. . . .

. . . .

2 marks

4

The table shows how many carpet tiles you need for some bigger floors.

	length of room				
	3m	**3½m**	**4m**	**4½m**	**5m**
3m	36	42	48	54	60
3½m	42	49	56	63	70
4m	48	56	64	72	80
4½m	54	63	72	81	90
5m	60	70	80	90	100

width of room

(b) Mr. Shan wants to carpet a floor that is **4m** by **5m**.

How many carpet tiles does he need?

1 mark

.... tiles

The shop sells the carpet tiles only in **packs of 10**.

How many packs of 10 should Mr. Shan buy?

1 mark

.... packs of 10

(c) Doctor Gee wants to carpet a floor that is **4m** by **3½m**.

How many carpet tiles does she need?

1 mark

.... tiles

How many packs of 10 should Doctor Gee buy?

1 mark

.... packs of 10

2.

The arrow on this thermometer shows a temperature of **10°C**.

(a) Draw an arrow on the thermometer to show a temperature of **24°C**.

Label the arrow 24°C.

(b) Draw an arrow on the thermometer to show a temperature of **−4°C**.

Label the arrow −4°C.

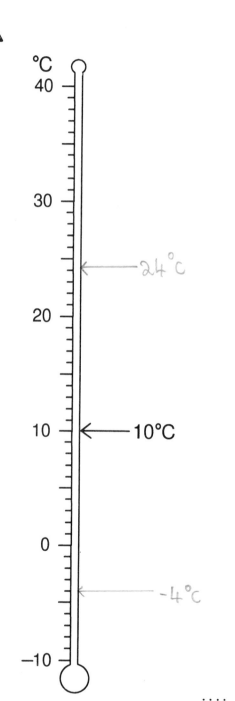

2 marks

(c) The temperature was **−10°C**.
It went **up 15°C**.
What is the temperature now?

.... °C

(d) Write these temperatures in order, **coldest first**.

| 3°C | −10°C | 0°C | 20°C | −1°C |

........°C   ....°C   ....°C   ....°C   ....°C

coldest   hottest

Gareth has some pegs and a pegboard.
He can make a **rectangle** with **18** pegs.

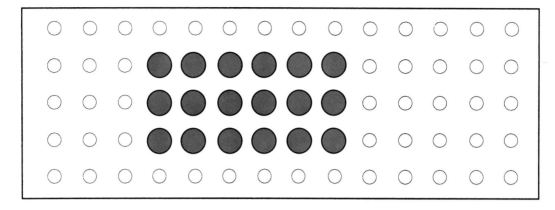

Gareth's rectangle is **6** pegs **long** and **3** pegs **wide**.

(a) Show how to use **18** pegs to make **another** rectangle
with a **different** shape.

The rectangle must be more than 1 peg long and more than 1 peg wide.

....
1 mark

How many pegs **long**
is your rectangle?

How many pegs **wide**
is your rectangle?

.... pegs **long**

.... pegs **wide**

....
1 mark

Gareth **cannot** make a rectangle with 5 pegs. He can only make a row. This is because **5** is a **prime number.**

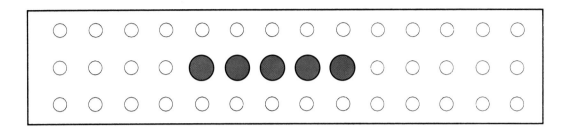

(b) Draw a row with a **prime number** of pegs which is **greater than 5**.

 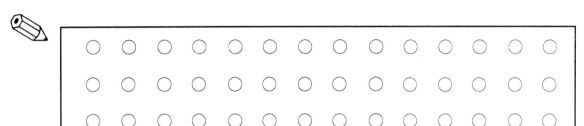

What is your prime number?

. . . .
1 mark

....

(c) Gareth says:

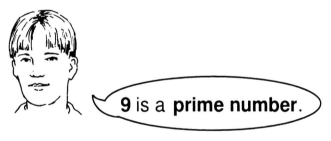

9 is a **prime number**.

Explain why Gareth is **wrong**.
You can write your answer, or draw a diagram.

. . . .
1 mark

Sue and Ben each have 12 biscuits.

(a)   Sue eats a **quarter** of her biscuits.

How many biscuits does Sue eat?

. . . .

1 mark

(b)   Ben eats **6** of his 12 biscuits.

What **fraction** of his biscuits does Ben eat?

. . . .

1 mark

(c)   **How many** biscuits are left altogether?

. . . .

1 mark

5.

(a) Fill in the missing numbers so that the answer is **always 45**.

The first one is done for you.

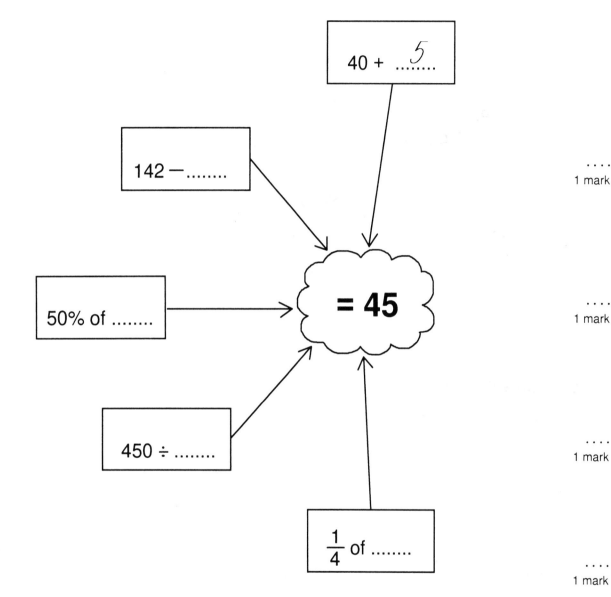

40 + ...*5*...

$$.\ .\ .\ .$$
1 mark

142 − ....

50% of ....

= 45

$$.\ .\ .\ .$$
1 mark

450 ÷ ....

$$.\ .\ .\ .$$
1 mark

$\frac{1}{4}$ of ....

$$.\ .\ .\ .$$
1 mark

(b) Fill in the gaps below to make the answer 45.

You may use any of these signs: +   −   ×   ÷

28 .... 2 .... 31 = 45

$$.\ .\ .\ .$$
1 mark

6.

(a) Look at this part of a number line:

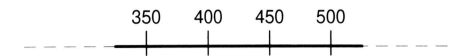

 Finish this sentence:

The numbers on this number line go **up** in steps of ....

. . . .
1 mark

(b) This is a **different** number line.
Fill in the 3 missing numbers.

. . . .
1 mark

(c) This is a **different** number line.
Fill in the 3 missing numbers.

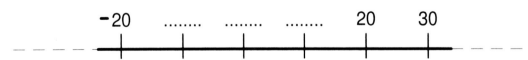

. . . .

. . . .
2 marks

(d) This is a **different** number line.
Fill in the 2 missing numbers.

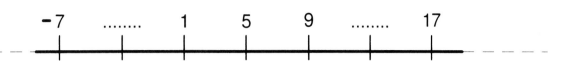

-7 .... 1 5 9 17

Finish this sentence:

The numbers on this number line go **up** in steps of ....

. . . .
. . . .
2 marks

(e) This is a **different** number line.
Fill in the 3 missing numbers.

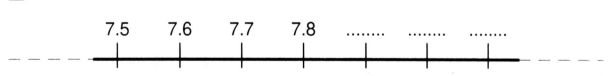

7.5 7.6 7.7 7.8 ....

. . . .
1 mark

Finish this sentence:

The numbers on this number line go **up** in steps of ....

. . . .
1 mark

Some board games have pegs in holes.

(a) On each board below, shade **5 more** pegs so that the dashed line is a **line of symmetry**.

You may use a mirror or tracing paper to help.

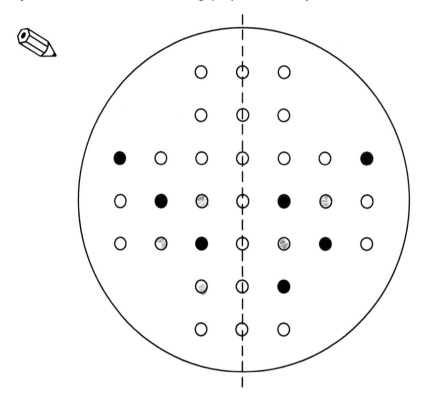

....
1 mark

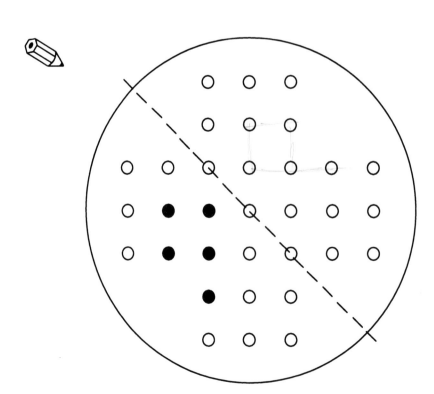

....
1 mark

(b) Shade **9 more** pegs so that **both** dashed lines are **lines of symmetry**.

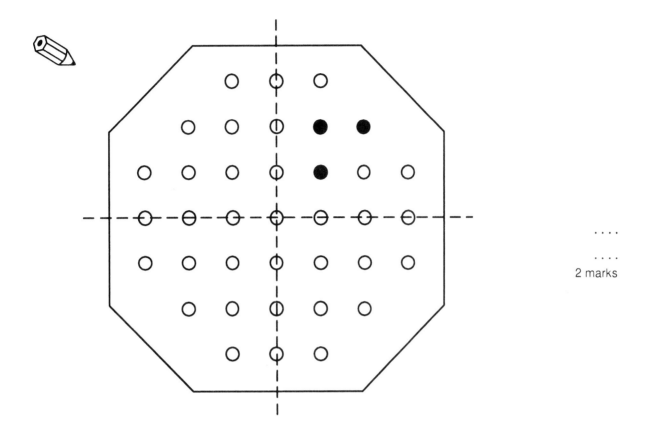

. . . .

. . . .

2 marks

15

$\frac{1}{2}$ of the diagram below is shaded.

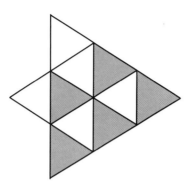

(a) Look at this diagram

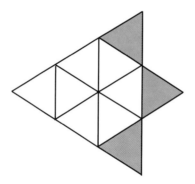

What **fraction** is shaded?

. . . .
1 mark

What **percentage** is shaded?

.... %

. . . .
1 mark

(b) Shade $\frac{2}{5}$ of the diagram below:

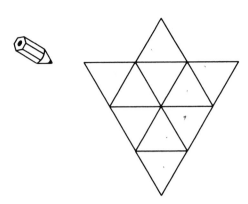

....
1 mark

What **percentage** of the diagram have you shaded?

.... %

....
1 mark

9.

Jenny is holding a row of cubes.

You cannot see exactly how many cubes she is holding.

Call the number of cubes she is holding n.

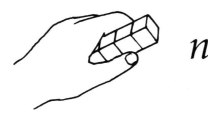

(a)   She joins on **two more** cubes.

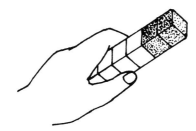

Write an expression for the total number of cubes she is holding now.

....

. . . .
1 mark

(b)   Jenny starts again with n cubes.
One cube is **removed**.
Write an expression for the total number of cubes she is holding now.

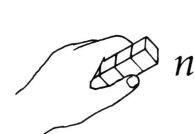 

....

. . . .
1 mark

one cube
removed

(c) Jenny starts again with **n** cubes.

Another row of the same length is **joined on**.

Write an expression for the total number of cubes she is holding now.

 **n**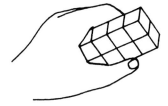

....

. . . .

another row
joined on

(d) Jacob also has some cubes in his hands.

In one hand there are **2n - 1** cubes.
In the other hand there are **2(n - 1)** cubes.

Is Jacob holding the same number of cubes in each hand?
Explain your answer.

. . . .

. . . .

10.

Karen and Huw each have three cards, numbered 2, 3, and 4.

They each take any **one** of their own cards.
Then they **add** together the numbers on the two cards.

The table shows all possible answers.

Karen

+	2	3	4
2	4	5	6
3	5	6	7
4	6	7	8

Huw (label for rows 2, 3, 4)

(a) What is the **probability** that their answer is an **even** number?

. . . .

1 mark

(b) What is the **probability** that their answer is
a number that is **greater than 6**?

. . . .

1 mark

(c) Both Karen and Huw still have their three cards, numbered 2, 3, and 4.

They each take any one of their own cards.
Then they **multiply** together the numbers on the two cards.

Draw a table to show all possible answers.

. . . .

1 mark

Use your table to fill in the gaps below:

The probability that their answer is a number that is

less than .... is $\frac{8}{9}$

. . . .

1 mark

The probability that their answer is a number that is

less than .... is **zero**.

. . . .

1 mark

Here are some algebra cards:

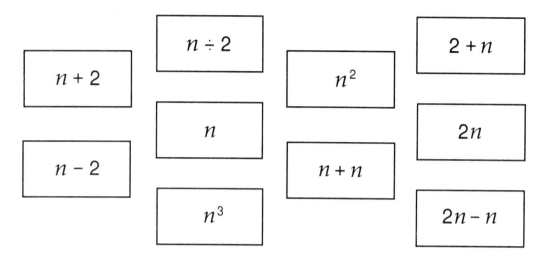

$n + 2$

$n \div 2$

n^2

$2 + n$

n

$2n$

$n - 2$

$n + n$

n^3

$2n - n$

(a) One of the cards will always give the same answer as

$$\dfrac{n}{2}$$

Which card is it?

. . . .
1 mark

....

(b) One of the cards will always give the same answer as

$n \times n$

Which card is it?

. . . .
1 mark

....

(c) **Two** of the cards will always give the same answer as

$$2 \times n$$

Which cards are they?

.... and ....

. . . .
. . . .
2 marks

(d) Write a **new** card which will always give the same answer as

$$3n + 2n$$

. . . .
1 mark

....

12.

Look at these number cards:

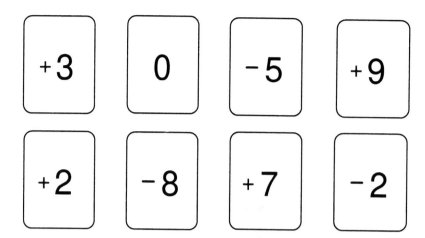

(a) Choose a card to give the answer 4.

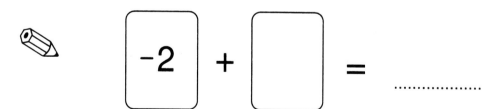

.....
1 mark

(b) Choose a card to give the **lowest** possible answer.

Fill in the card below and work out the answer.

-2 + ☐ = ...

....
....
2 marks

(c) Choose a card to give the **lowest** possible answer.

Fill in the card below and work out the answer.

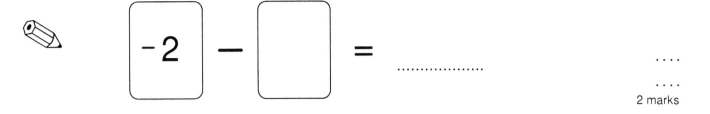

$\boxed{-2} - \boxed{} = \text{.................}$

. . . .

. . . .

2 marks

(d) Now choose a card to give the **highest** possible answer.

Fill in the card below and work out the answer.

$\boxed{-2} - \boxed{} = \text{.................}$

. . . .

. . . .

2 marks

13.

(a) A shop sells plants.

95p each

Find the cost of **35** plants.

Show your working.

Cost is £ ....

. . . .

. . . .

2 marks

(b) The shop also sells trees.

£17 each

Mr. Bailey has **£250**
He wants to buy as many trees as possible.

How many trees can Mr. Bailey buy?

Show your working.

.... trees

. . . .

. . . .

2 marks

A child is having a bath.

The simplified graph shows the depth of water in the bath.

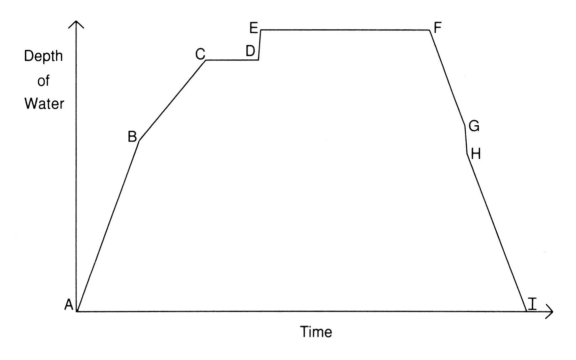

(a) From A to B **both taps** are turned **full on**.
What might be happening at point B?

. . . .
1 mark

(b) Which part of the graph shows the child getting into the bath?

. . . .
1 mark

..........E.. to ....F.....

(c) Which part of the graph shows the child getting out of the bath?

. . . .
1 mark

..........F.. to ....G.....

Kay is drawing shapes on her computer.

(a) She wants to draw this triangle. She needs to know angles *a*, *b* and *c*.

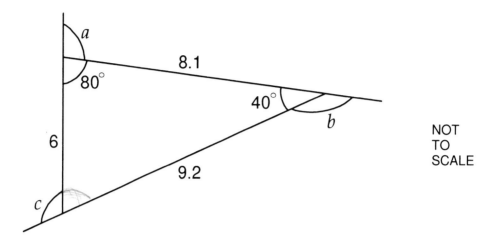

NOT
TO
SCALE

Calculate angles *a*, *b* and *c*.

a = ...100.......°

. . . .
1 mark

b = ...140.......°

c = ...120.......°

. . . .
1 mark

(b) Kay draws a rhombus:

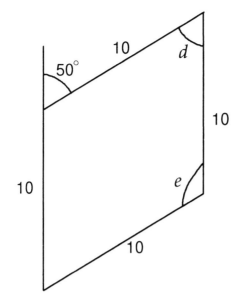

10

50°

d

10

10

NOT
TO
SCALE

10

e

10

Calculate angles d and e.

d = ...50......°

....
1 mark

e = ...13......°

....
1 mark

(c) Kay types the instructions to draw a regular pentagon:

repeat 5 [forward 10, left turn 72]

Complete the instructions to draw a regular hexagon.

repeat 6 [forward 10, left turn ....]

....
1 mark

16.

(a) James has these four number cards:

| 1 | 8 | 5 | 2 |

The **mean** is 4.

James takes another card.

| 1 | 8 | 5 | 2 | 4 ? |

The mean of the **five** cards is still 4.

What number is on his new card?

4

. . . .
1 mark

(b) Tara has these four number cards:

| 10 | 3 | 2 | 5 |

She takes another card.

| 10 | 3 | 2 | 5 | ? |

The mean goes **up** by **2**.

What number is on her new card?

Show your working.

....

. . . .

. . . .

2 marks

(c) Ali has six cards.

| 10 | 10 | 10 | 10 | ? | ? |

The **mean** of the six cards is **10**.

The **range** of the six cards is **4**.

What are the numbers on the other two cards?

.... and ....

. . . .

1 mark

Look at this octagon:

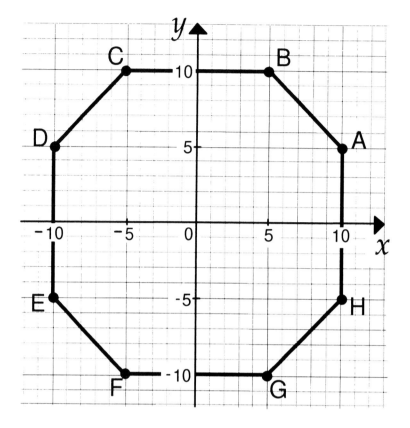

(a) The line through A and H has the equation $x = 10$

What is the equation of the line through **F** and **G**?

. . . .

1 mark

....

(b) Fill in the gaps below:

$x + y = 15$ is the equation of the line through .... and ....

. . . .

1 mark

(c) The octagon has four lines of symmetry.

One of the lines of symmetry has the equation $y = x$

On the diagram, draw **and label** the line $y = x$

. . . .

1 mark

(d) The octagon has three **other** lines of symmetry.

Write the equation of **one** of these three **other** lines of symmetry.

....

1 mark

....

(e) The line through D and B has the equation $3y = x + 25$

The line through G and H has the equation $x = y + 15$

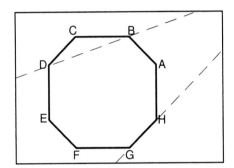

Solve the simultaneous equations

$$3y = x + 25$$

$$x = y + 15$$

Show your working.

....

....

2 marks

$x =$ .... $y =$ ....

(f) Complete this sentence:

The line through D and B meets

....

the line through G and H at (........... , ...)

1 mark

18.

The scatter diagram shows the total amounts of sunshine and rainfall for 12 seaside towns during one summer.
Each town has been given a letter.

The dashed lines drawn go through the **mean** amounts of sunshine and rainfall.

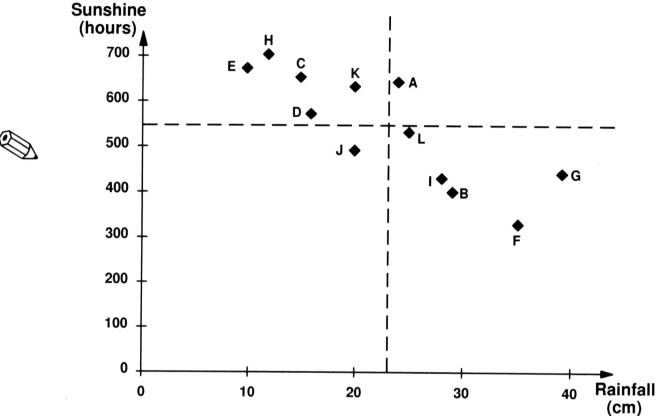

(a) Which town's rainfall was closest to the mean?

Town ....
. . . .
1 mark

(b) Draw a **line of best fit** on the scatter diagram.

. . . .

. . . .
2 marks

Use your line to find an estimate of the hours of sunshine for a seaside town that had 30cm of rain.

.... hours
. . . .
1 mark

For each of these cards n can be any positive number.

The **answers** given by the cards are all positive numbers.

$$n^2 \qquad 0.8\,n \qquad \sqrt{n} \qquad \dfrac{n}{0.8} \qquad \dfrac{1}{n}$$

(a) Which card will **always** give an answer **less than** n?

. . . .

1 mark

(b) When n **is 1**, which cards will give the answer **1**?

. . . .

. . . .

2 marks

(c) When n **is 4**, which cards will give an answer **less than 4**?

. . . .

. . . .

2 marks

(d) When n **is less than 1**, which cards will give an answer **less than** n?

. . . .

. . . .

2 marks

On a farm many years ago the water tanks were filled using a bucket from a well.

(a) The table shows the numbers of buckets, of different capacities, needed to fill a tank of capacity 2400 pints.

Complete the table:

Capacity of bucket (pints)	8	10	12	15	16		
Number of buckets			200		150	100	80

. . . .
. . . .
. . . .
3 marks

(b) Write an equation using symbols to connect **T**, the capacity of the tank, **B**, the capacity of a bucket, and **N**, the number of buckets.

. . . .
1 mark

(c) Now tanks are filled through a hosepipe connected to a tap. The rate of flow through the hosepipe can be varied.

A tank of capacity **4000** litres fills at a rate of **12.5** litres per minute. How long in hours and minutes does it take to fill the tank?

Show your working.

.... hours .... minutes

. . . .
. . . .
2 marks

(d) Another tank took **5 hours** to fill at **a different rate** of flow.
How long would it have taken to fill this tank if this rate of flow had been increased by **100%**?

.... hours .... minutes

. . . .
1 mark

(e) How long would it have taken to fill this tank if the rate of flow had been increased by only **50%**?

Show your working.

. . . .

. . . .
2 marks

.... hours .... minutes

(f) This tank, measuring *a* by *b* by *c*, takes 1 hour 15 minutes to fill.

How long does it take to fill a tank **2a** by **2b** by **2c**, at the same rate of flow?

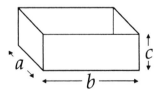

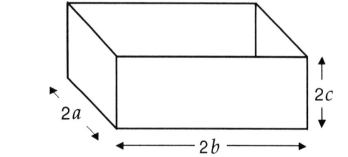

Show your working.

. . . .

. . . .
2 marks

21.

40 students worked on a farm one weekend. The cumulative frequency graph shows the distribution of the amount of money they earned. No one earned less than £15.

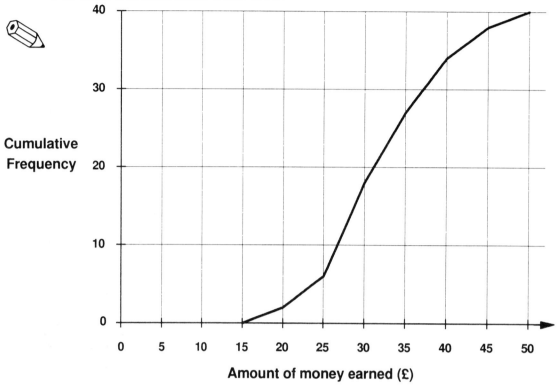

(a) Read the graph to estimate the **median** amount of money earned.

. . . .
1 mark

Median £ ....

(b) Estimate the **percentage** of students who earned **less than £40**.

. . . .
1 mark

.......................%

(c) Show on the graph how to work out the **interquartile range** of the amount of money earned.

. . . .
1 mark

Write down the value of the interquartile range.

. . . .
1 mark

Interquartile range £ ....

(d) 30 of the students work on the farm another weekend later in the year.
The tables below show the distribution of the amount of money earned by
the students.

Money earned (£)	No. of students
≥ 25 and < 30	1
≥ 30 and < 35	2
≥ 35 and < 40	3
≥ 40 and < 45	4
≥ 45 and < 50	10
≥ 50 and < 55	7
≥ 55 and < 60	3

Money earned (£)	No. of students
< 25	0
< 30	1
< 35	3
< 40	6
< 45	10
< 50	20
< 55	27
< 60	30

Draw a cumulative frequency graph using the axes below.

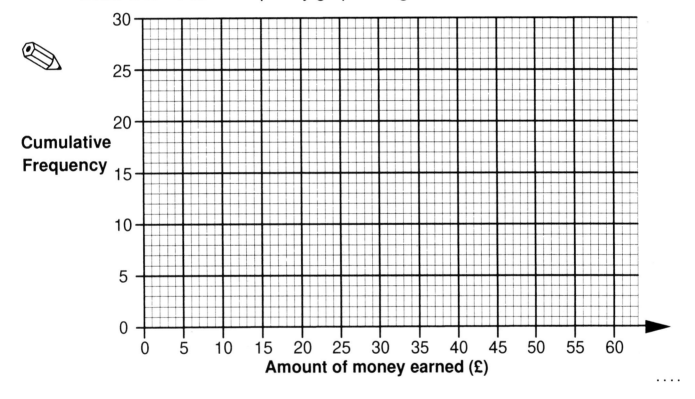

Cumulative
Frequency

Amount of money earned (£)

. . . .

. . . .

2 marks

(e) Put a ✓ by any statement below which is true.
Put a ✗ by any statement below which is false.

A. Three of the students earned less than £35 each.   . . . .

B. The median amount earned is between £40 and £45.   . . . .

. . . .

1 mark

C. Most of the 30 students earned more than £50 each.   . . . .

Alan throws a ball to Katie who is standing 20m away.
The ball is thrown and caught at a height of 2.0m above the ground.

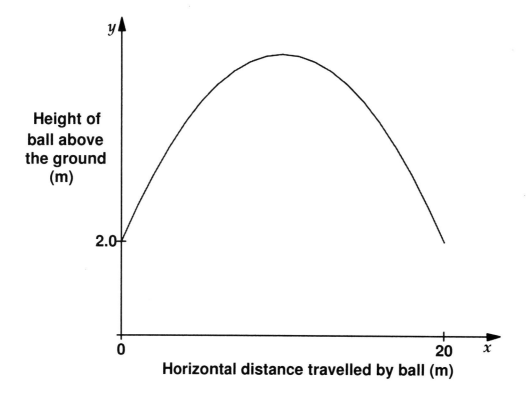

The ball follows the curve with equation

$$y = 6 + c(10 - x)^2 \quad \text{where c is a constant.}$$

(a) Calculate the value of c by substituting $x = 0$, $y = 2$ into the equation.

Show your working.

. . . .

. . . .

. . . .

3 marks

C = ...

Alan throws the ball to Katie again, but this time the ball hits the ground before it reaches her.

The ball follows the curve with equation $y = -0.1(x^2 - 6x - 16)$

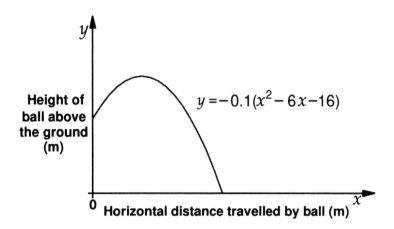

(b) Calculate the height above the ground at which the ball left Alan's hand.

Show your working.

....

....

....

3 marks

.... m

END OF TEST

Combined Paper 2 Questions, Levels 3–8

Write your name and school in the spaces below.

First Name _____

Last Name _____

School _____

Remember

- Answer as many questions as you can in 1 hour. You are *not* expected to answer all the questions.

- You may use a calculator for any question in this test, if you want to.

- You will need: pen, pencil, rubber, ruler, scientific or graphic calculator, angle measurer or protractor and pair of compasses.

- Some formulae you might need are on page 3.

- This test starts with easier questions.

- Write all your answers and working on the test paper - do not use any rough paper.

- Check your work carefully.

- Ask if you are not sure what to do.

Instructions

Answers

 This means:
write down your answer.

Calculators

 You **may** use a calculator to
answer any question in this test
if you want to.

Formulae

You might need to use these formulae.

AREA

Rectangle

length × width

Circle

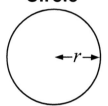

πr^2

Take π as 3.14

Triangle

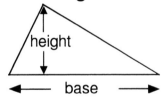

$\dfrac{\text{base} \times \text{height}}{2}$

Parallelogram

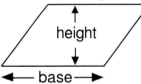

base × height

Trapezium

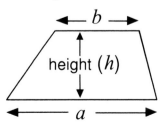

$\dfrac{(a + b)}{2} \times h$

LENGTH

Circle

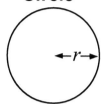

circumference $= 2\pi r$

For a right-angled triangle

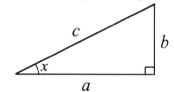

$a^2 + b^2 = c^2$ (Pythagoras' theorem)

$a = c \cos x \qquad \cos\ x = \dfrac{a}{c}$

$b = c \sin x \qquad \sin\ x = \dfrac{b}{c}$

$b = a \tan x \qquad \tan\ x = \dfrac{b}{a}$

VOLUME

Prism

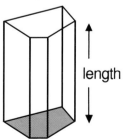

area of cross-section × length

Lyn recorded the temperature at lunch time every day for a week.
She started to draw a bar chart to show her results.

(a) The temperature on **Friday** was **25°C**.
The temperature on **Saturday** was **19°C**.

Draw the bars for **Friday** and **Saturday** on Lyn's bar chart.

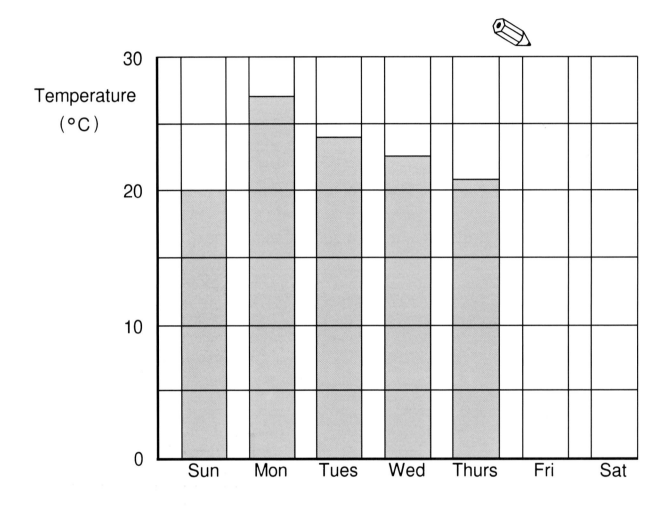

. . . .

. . . .

2 marks

What was the temperature on **Monday**?

.... °C

. . . .

1 mark

(b) Five more pupils recorded the temperature every day
for different weeks in the year.

Match the pupils to their bar charts on the next page.
The first is done for you.

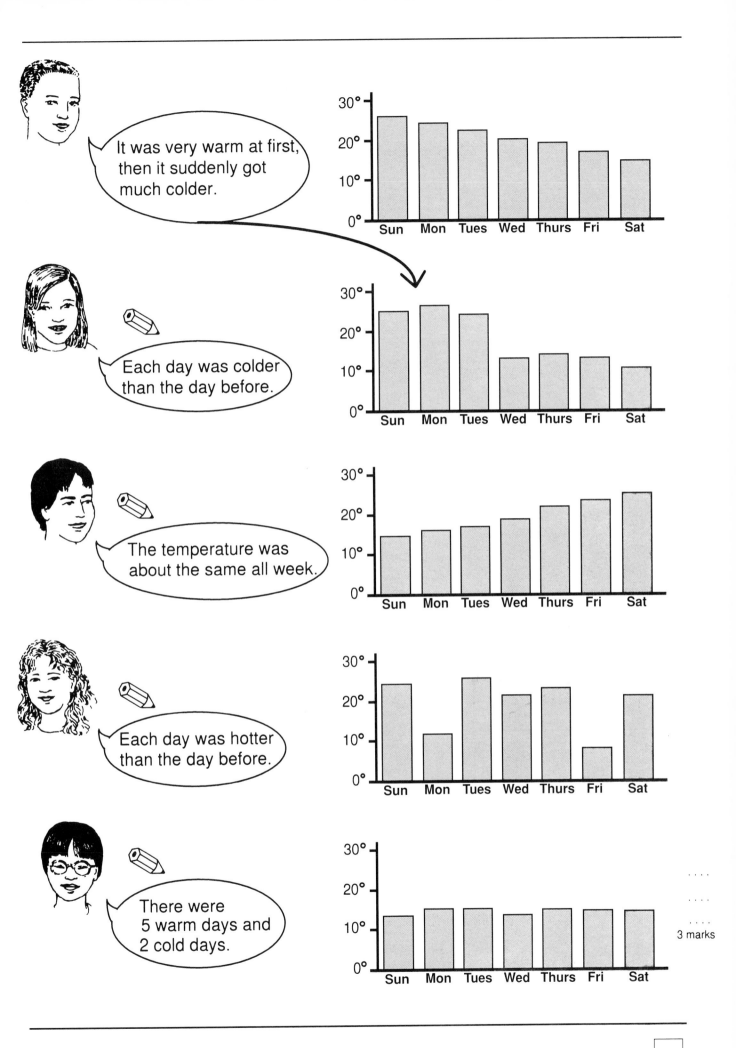

3 marks

Mike has a triangle grid.

He shades in **2 triangles** to make a shape with **4 sides**.

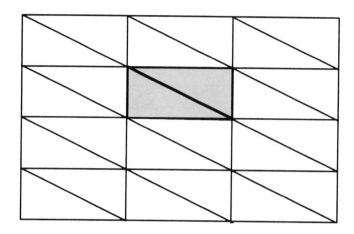

(a) Shade in **2 triangles** on this grid
to make a **different** shape
with 4 sides.

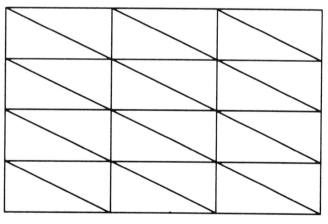

(b) Shade in **2 triangles** on this grid
to make another **different** shape
with 4 sides.

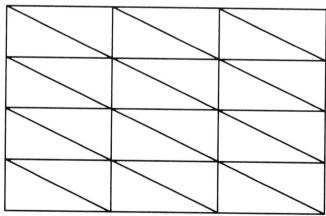

. . . .

. . . .

2 marks

6

(c) Shade in **4** small triangles on this grid to make a **bigger triangle**.

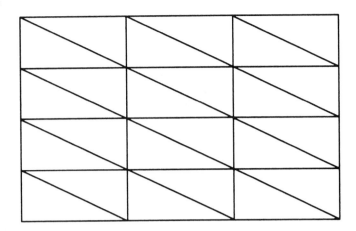

. . . .
1 mark

(d) Shade in **more than 4** small triangles on this grid to make a **bigger triangle**.

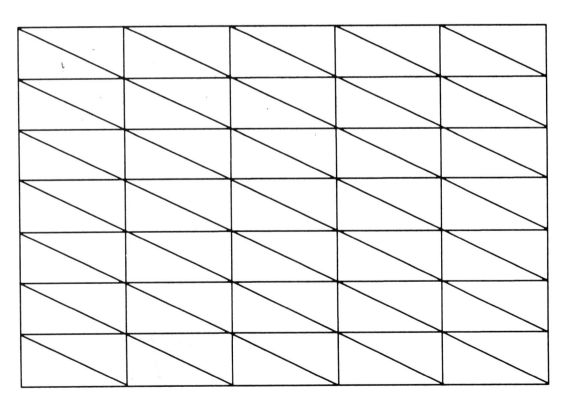

. . . .
1 mark

3.

(a) Lucy had dinner.
It cost **£13.40**
She paid with a **£20** note.

How much **change** should Lucy get?

£ . . . .

1 mark

(b) **14** people had the set meal at the cafe.

How much did they pay altogether?

£ . . . .

1 mark

set meal
£6.40
each

Another group of people had the set meal.
Altogether they paid **£32**.

How many people were in the group?

....

. . . .

1 mark

4.

This table shows the distances by road between some towns.

Distances in miles:

Hull				
Exeter	305			
Bangor	199	289		
Dover	261	248	331	
	Hull	**Exeter**	**Bangor**	**Dover**

(a) Which **two** towns are the **shortest distance** from each other?

....
1 mark

.... and ....

(b) Mrs. Davis drove from Bangor to Exeter.

What is the distance between **Bangor** and **Exeter**?

....
1 mark

.... miles

Then Mrs. Davis drove from Exeter to Dover.

What is the distance between **Exeter** and **Dover**?

....
1 mark

.... miles

How far did Mrs. Davis drive altogether?

....
1 mark

.... miles

5

The grid shows the first eight lines of a spiral pattern.

The spiral pattern starts at the point marked ■

(a) Continue the spiral by drawing the **next four lines** on the grid below.

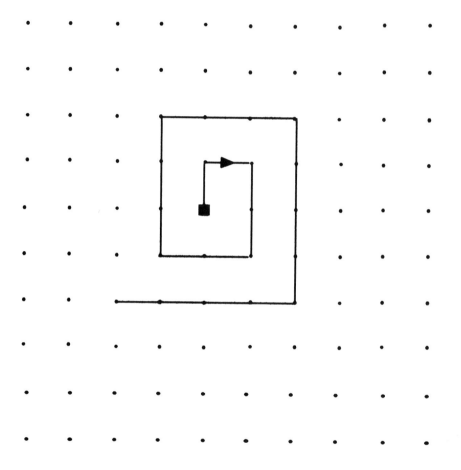

. . . .

1 mark

(b) The table shows the length of each line.

line number	length
1	1
2	1
3	2
4	2
5	3
6	3
7	4
8	4
9	5

The rule for finding the length of **odd** numbered lines is:

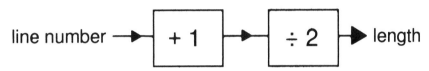

What is the length of line number **23**?

....

(c) Fill in the box to show the rule for finding
     the length of **even** numbered lines.

(d) What is the length of line number **18**?

....

6.

(a) Carl is putting packs of biscuits into a box.

He starts to put in the bottom layer.

The box holds **5 packs across** and is **4 packs wide**.

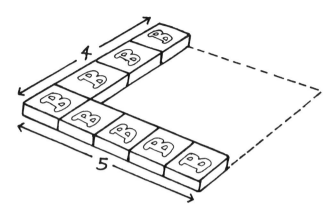

How many packs will fit altogether on the bottom layer?

.... packs

. . . .
1 mark

The box holds **6 layers**.

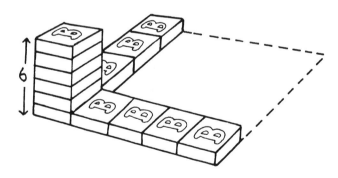

How many packs will fit in the box when it is **full**?

. . . .
1 mark

.... packs

12

(b) Aziz is putting packs of tea into a box.

The box holds **5 packs across** and is **6 packs wide**.
The box holds **3 layers**.

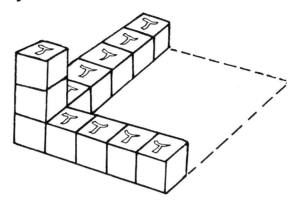

How many packs of tea will fit in the box when it is **full**?

.... packs

(c) Fill in the gaps below to show one way of filling
a **different** box with **24** packs in **2** layers.

total: 24 packs

2 layers

.... packs across

.... packs wide

(a) Here is a number chain:

$$2 \longrightarrow 4 \longrightarrow 6 \longrightarrow 8 \longrightarrow 10 \longrightarrow 12 \longrightarrow$$

The rule is: **add on 2 each time**

A different number chain is:

$$2 \longrightarrow 4 \longrightarrow 8 \longrightarrow 16 \longrightarrow 32 \longrightarrow 64 \longrightarrow$$

What could the rule be?

. . . .

1 mark

(b) Some number chains start like this:

$$1 \longrightarrow 5 \longrightarrow$$

Show three **different** ways to continue this number chain.

For each chain write down the next three numbers.
Then write down the rule you are using.

first chain:

   $1 \longrightarrow 5 \longrightarrow \ldots\ldots \longrightarrow \ldots\ldots \longrightarrow \ldots\ldots$

The rule is: ....

. . . .

1 mark

second chain:

    1 → 5 → ...... → ...... → ......

The rule is: ....

. . . .

1 mark

third chain:

    1 → 5 → ...... → ...... → ......

The rule is: ....

. . . .

1 mark

(a)   Joe has these cards:

Sara takes a card without looking.

Joe says:

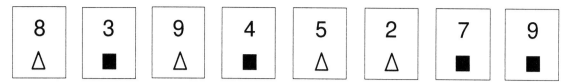

> On Sara's card,
> ■ is **more likely** than △

Explain why Joe is **wrong**.

. . . .
1 mark

Here are some words and phrases:

impossible	not likely	certain	likely

Choose a word or phrase to fill in the gaps below.

It is .... that the number on Sara's card will be **smaller than 10**.

. . . .
1 mark

It is .... that the number on Sara's card will be an **odd number**.

. . . .
1 mark

(b) Joe still has these cards:

| 8 △ | 3 ■ | 9 △ | 4 ■ | 5 △ | 2 △ | 7 ■ | 9 ■ |

He mixes them up and puts them face down on the table.
Then he turns the first card over, like this:

| 5 △ |

Joe is going to turn the next card over.

Complete this sentence:

On the next card, ... is **less likely** than ....

. . . .
1 mark

The number on the next card could be higher than 5 or lower than 5.
Which is **more likely**?

Tick the correct box.

☐ higher than 5　　☐ lower than 5　　☐ cannot tell

Explain your answer.

. . . .
1 mark

9.

(a) The scale shows how long Laura was when she was born.

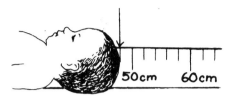

How long was Laura?

.... cm

. . . .
1 mark

(b) When Laura was one month old she was put on the scales.

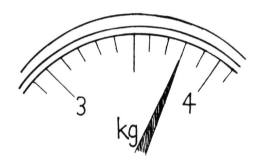

What mass do the scales show?

.... kg

. . . .
1 mark

(c) Now Laura is older.
She is **1.03m** tall.
Write Laura's height in centimetres.

. . . .
1 mark

.... cm

There are **50 children** altogether in a playgroup.

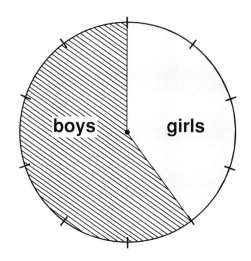

(a) **How many** of the children are **girls**?

....
                                                                             1 mark

What **percentage** of the children are girls?

.... %   . . . .
                                                                             1 mark

(b) **25** of the children are **4 years old**.
     20 of the children are **3 years old**.
      5 of the children are **2 years old**.

     Show this information on the diagram below.
     Label each part clearly.

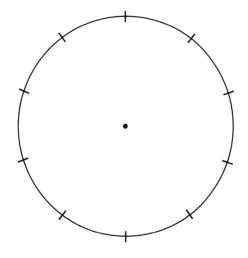

                                                                              . . . .

                                                                              . . . .

                                                                              . . . .
                                                                             3 marks

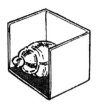

Alex is making a box to display a shell.

The base of the box is shaded.

He draws the **net** of the box like this:

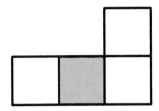

Alex wants to put a lid on the box.

He must add one more square to his net.

(a) On each diagram below, show a **different** place to add the new square. Remember, the **base** of the box is **shaded**.

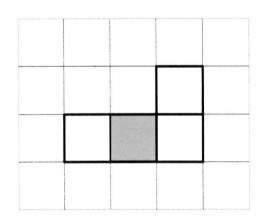

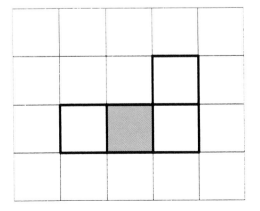

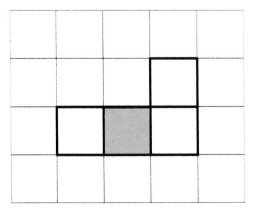

. . . .

. . . .

. . . .

3 marks

Alex makes a different box with
a lid hinged at the top.

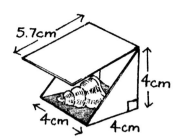

The base of his box is shaded.

He starts to draw a full size net.

(b) Complete his diagram below **accurately**.

. . . .

. . . .

. . . .

3 marks

The Highway Code states the minimum distance there should be between cars. There are different distances for bad weather and good weather.

The graph below shows this.

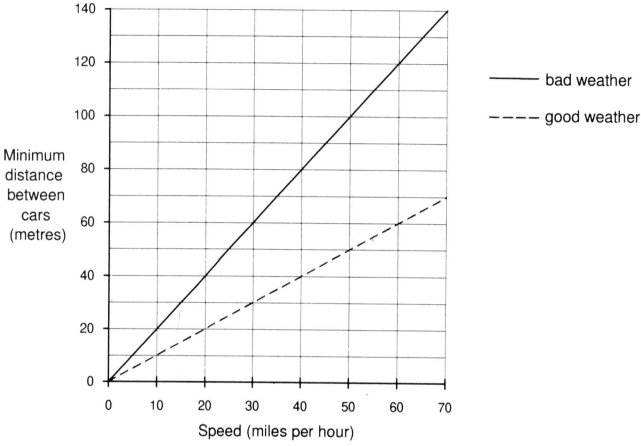

bad weather

---- good weather

(a) The weather is **bad**.
A car is travelling at **40 miles per hour**.

What is the minimum distance it should be from the car in front?

.... metres

. . . .
1 mark

(b) The weather is **good**.
A car is travelling at **55 miles per hour**.

What is the minimum distance it should be from the car in front?

.... metres

. . . .
1 mark

(c) Mr. Evans is driving **30 metres** behind another car.
     The weather is **bad**.

     What is the maximum speed at which Mr. Evans should be driving?

. . . .

1 mark

.... miles per hour

(d) Mrs. Singh is driving at **50 miles per hour** in good weather.
     She is the minimum distance from the car in front.

     It begins to rain heavily.
     Both cars slow down to **30 miles per hour**.

     Use the graph to work out how much Mrs. Singh must increase her
     distance from the car in front.

     Show your working.

.... metres

. . . .

. . . .

2 marks

Here is a **rough sketch** of a sector of a circle.

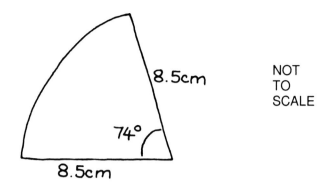

NOT
TO
SCALE

Make an **accurate**, **full size** drawing of this sector.

. . . .

. . . .

. . . .

. . . .

4 marks

The cost of an old toy vehicle depends on its condition and on whether it is in its original box.

Condition	Value
excellent, and in its box	100%
good, and in its box	85%
poor, and in its box	50%
excellent, but not in its box	65%
good, but not in its box	32%
poor, but not in its box	15%

A Mail Van in excellent condition, and in its box, costs **£125**.

(a) How much is a Mail Van in **good** condition, and in its box?

. . . .
1 mark

£ ....

(b) How much is a Mail Van in **good** condition, **but not in its box**?

. . . .
1 mark

£ ....

(c) A Petrol Tanker in excellent condition, and in its box, costs £152.

Another Petrol Tanker should be sold for £98.80
Using the chart above, what is its condition and does it have its box?

. . . .
1 mark

Some pupils wanted to find out if people liked a new biscuit.
They decided to do a survey and wrote a questionnaire.

(a) One question was:

How old are you (in years)?

☐ ☐ ☐ ☐ ☐

20 or younger   20 to 30   30 to 40   40 to 50   50 or older

Mary said:

> The labels for the middle three boxes need changing.

Explain why Mary was **right**.

. . . .

1 mark

(b) A different question was:

How much do you usually spend on biscuits each week?

☐ a lot   ☐ a little   ☐ nothing   ☐ don't know

Mary said: "Some of these labels need changing too".

Write new labels for any boxes that need changing.
You may change as many labels as you want to.

☐ .... ☐ .... ☐ .... ☐ ....

. . . .

. . . .

2 marks

The pupils decide to give their questionnaire to 50 people.
Jon said:

(c) Give **one disadvantage** of Jon's suggestion.

. . . .
1 mark

(d) Give **one advantage** of Jon's suggestion.

. . . .
1 mark

16.

This prism is made from 6 cubes.

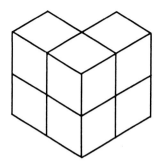

The piece of paper below fits exactly around the **sides** of the prism.

The **dashed** lines are **fold** lines.

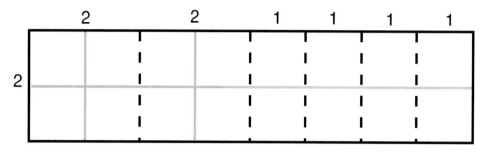

(a) A different prism is made from 10 cubes.

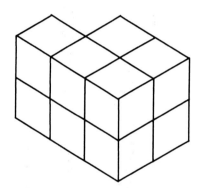

Complete the diagram below to show a piece of paper that fits exactly around the sides of the 10 cube prism.

Show all fold lines as dashed lines.

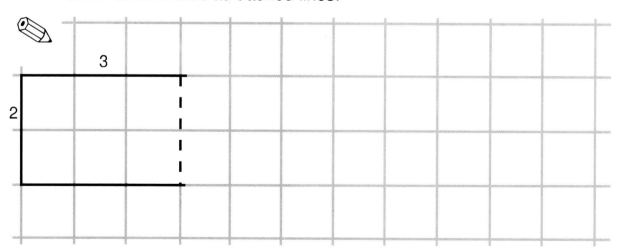

. . . .

. . . .

2 marks

28

(b) The piece of paper below fits exactly around the sides of a 14 cube prism.

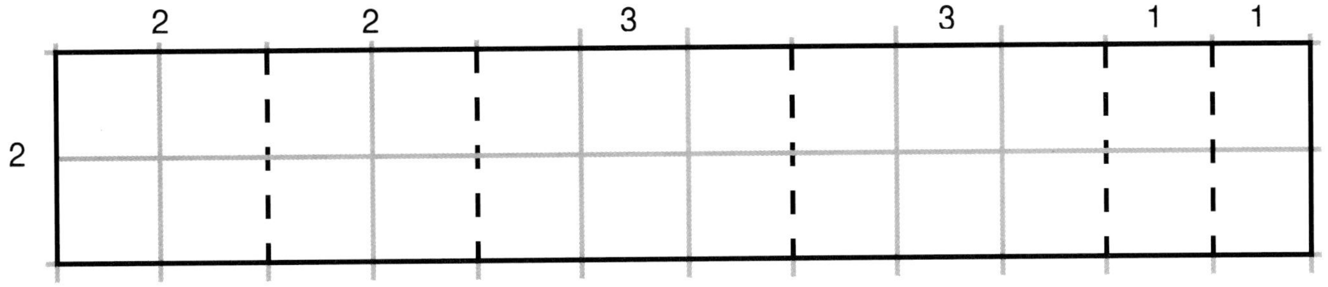

	2	2	3	3	1	1

2

Draw this 14 cube prism below.

. . . .

. . . .

. . . .

3 marks

17.

In these walls each brick is made by **adding** the **two** bricks underneath it.

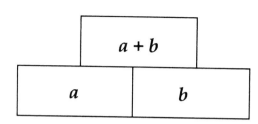

(a) Write an expression for the top brick in this wall.
Write your expression as simply as possible.

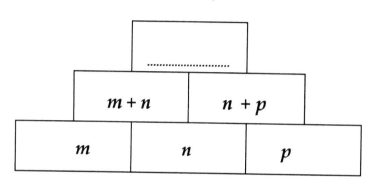

. . . .
1 mark

(b) Fill in the missing expressions on these walls.
Write your expressions as simply as possible.

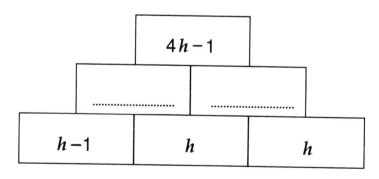

. . . .
. . . .
2 marks

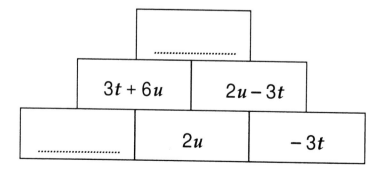

. . . .
. . . .
2 marks

(c) In the wall below, h, j and k can be any whole numbers.

Explain why the top brick of the wall must **always** be an **even** number.

You can fill in the missing expressions if you want to.

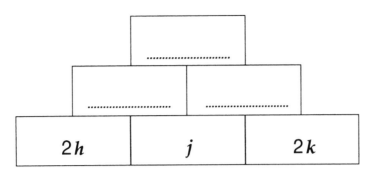

. . . .

. . . .

2 marks

The table shows some information about pupils in a school.

	left-handed	right-handed
girls	32	180
boys	28	168

There are **408 pupils** in the school.

(a) What **percentage** of the pupils are **boys**?
Show your working.

.... %

. . . .

. . . .

2 marks

(b) What is the **ratio** of **left-handed** pupils to **right-handed** pupils?
Write your ratio in the form 1 : ......
Show your working.

. . . .

. . . .

2 marks

(c) One pupil is chosen at random from the whole school.
What is the **probability** that the pupil chosen
is a **girl** who is **right-handed**?

. . . .

1 mark

19.

Calculate the area of this triangle.

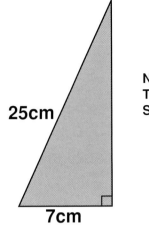

NOT
TO
SCALE

25cm

7cm

Show your working.

Area of triangle = ... cm²

· · · ·

· · · ·

· · · ·

3 marks

Some pupils want to plant a tree in the school's garden.

The tree must be at least **12m** from the school buildings.

It must also be at least **10m** from the **centre** of the round pond.

(a)   Show accurately on the plan the **region** in which the tree can
be planted.

Shade in this region.

SCALE   1cm to 2m

Pond

2m

School
Buildings

Fence

. . . .

. . . .

. . . .

3 marks

(b)   The pupils want to make a gravel path of width **1m** around the pond.

Calculate the **area** of the path.

Show your working.

. . . .

. . . .

2 marks

.....................m²

21.

A company makes breakfast cereal containing nuts and raisins.

They counted the number of nuts and raisins in 100 small packets.

Results

Chart A: Nuts

Chart B: Raisins

(a) Calculate an estimate of the **mean** number of **nuts** in a packet.
Show your working.
You may complete the table below to help you with the calculation.

Number of nuts	Mid-point of bar (x)	Number of packets (f)	fx
4 - 6	5	26	130
7 - 9	8	33	
10 - 12	11	20	
13 - 15	14	15	
16 - 18	17	6	
		100	

....

....

2 marks

.... nuts

36

(b) Calculate an estimate of the **number** of packets that contain **24 or more raisins**.

. . . .
. . . .
2 marks

.... packets

(c) Which of the two charts shows the **greater range**?
Explain your answer.

. . . .
1 mark

(d) A packet is chosen at random.
Calculate the probability that it contains **9 nuts or fewer**.

. . . .
1 mark

(e) The number of raisins in a packet is independent of the number of nuts.
A packet is chosen at random.
Calculate the probability that it contains 16 to 18 nuts **and** 6 to 10 raisins.
Show your working.

. . . .
. . . .
2 marks

The compactness value, C, of a shape can be calculated using the formula:

$$C = \frac{4A}{\pi K^2}$$

The **area** of the shape is **A**.

The **distance** between two points in the shape that are **furthest apart** is **K**.

(a) **Calculate** the compactness value for this square.

(The distance K is the length of a diagonal.)

Show your working.

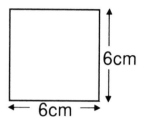

. . . .

. . . .

. . . .

3 marks

Compactness value ....

(b) **Calculate** the compactness value for this rectangle.

Show your working.

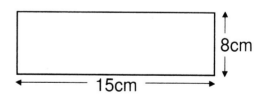

. . . .

. . . .

2 marks

Compactness value ....

(c) **Calculate** the compactness value for this rhombus.

(An angle is given for you to use in your calculation.)

Show your working.

```
            /\
           /  \
          /    |
         /     |
        / - - - + 30°\
        \     | 'L    /
         \    |      /
          \   |     /
           \  |    /
            \ |  /
             \|/
      ←——— 10cm ———→
```

. . . .

. . . .

. . . .

3 marks

Compactness value ....

(d) Calculate the compactness value of a circle with radius 3cm.

(The distance K is the length of a diameter.)

Show your working.

. . . .

. . . .

2 marks

Compactness value ....

(e) What is the compactness value of a circle with radius R?

. . . .

1 mark

Compactness value ....

Two buses travel along the same route from the Town Hall to the Red Lion, 8km away, and back again.

This simplified graph shows the journeys.
P and Q mark two points on the graph.

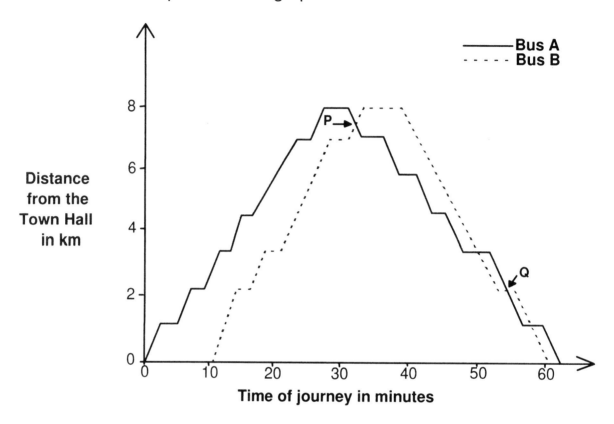

(a) Describe briefly what happened at point P.

. . . .

1 mark

(b) Describe briefly what happened at point Q.

. . . .

1 mark

Bus A took 27 minutes to get to the Red Lion.

(c) Work out the average speed in km per hour.

.... km per hour

1 mark

(d) Bus A stopped several times on the way to the Red Lion.
The average time for a stop was 2 minutes.

Work out the average speed using **only** that amount of **time** during which the bus was **moving** in your calculation.

Show your working.

.... km per hour

2 marks

(e) Bus B went at an average speed of 21.5 km per hour back to the Town Hall.
Work out the average speed in **miles per hour**.

Show your working.

.... miles per hour

2 marks

> Speed of light is about 1.1×10^9 km per hour
>
> Speed of sound is about 1.2×10^3 km per hour

(a) Calculate the speed of light in km per second.
     Give your answer in standard form.

     Show your working.

                                                                    . . . .

                                                                    . . . .
                                                                   2 marks
                          .... km per second

(b) How many times as fast as the speed of sound is the speed of light?
     Give your answer to an appropriate degree of accuracy.

     Show your working.

                                                                    . . . .

                                                                    . . . .
                                                                   2 marks

(c) Gary sees a flash of lightning.
25 seconds later he hears the sound of thunder.

Calculate how far away he is from the lightning.
(You do **not** need to include the speed of light in your calculation.)

Show your working.

. . . .

. . . .

2 marks

.... km

END OF TEST

Mark Scheme for Papers 1 and 2, Levels 3–8

Introduction

This guidance on marking is provided to help parents in assessing their childs answers to the questions. It includes the mark scheme for papers 1 and 2 at Levels 3-8. Questions have been given names so that each one has a unique identifier along with its number.

The structure of the mark scheme

The marking information for questions is set out in the form tables, which start on page 4. The column on the left hand side of each table provides a quick reference to the question number, question part, and the total number of marks available for that question part.

The **'Correct response'** column usually includes two types of information:

- a statement of the requirements for the award of each mark,
  with an indication of whether credit can be given for correct working,
  and whether the marks are independent or cumulative;

- examples of some different types of correct response,
  including the most common and the minimum acceptable.

The **'Additional guidance'** column indicates alternative acceptable responses, and provides details of specific types of response which are unacceptable. Other guidance, such as when 'follow through' is allowed, is provided as necessary.

For graphical and diagrammatic responses, including those in which degrees of accuracy are hard to judge, marking overlays have been provided in a separate pad.

Using the mark schemes

Answers that are numerically equivalent or algebraically equivalent are acceptable unless the marks scheme states otherwise. The most frequent procedural queries are listed below with the prescribed correct action. Unless otherwise specified in the mark scheme, markers should apply the following guidelines in all cases.

What if . . .

The pupil's response does not match closely any of the examples given.	Markers should use their judgement in deciding whether the response corresponds with the statement of requirements given in the 'Correct response' column. Refer also to the additional guidance, and if still uncertain contact the supervising marker.
The pupil has responded in a non-standard way.	Calculations, formulae and written responses do not have to be set out in any particular format. Pupils may provide evidence in any form as long as its meaning can be understood. Diagrams, symbols or words are acceptable for explanations or for indicating a response. Any correct method of setting out working, however idiosyncratic, is acceptable.
The pupil's accuracy is marginal according to the overlay provided.	Overlays can never be 100% accurate. However, provided the answer is within, or touches, the boundaries given, the mark(s) should be awarded. If still in doubt, markers should check with appropriate measuring equipment.
The pupil's answer correctly follows through from earlier incorrect work.	'Follow through' marks may be awarded only when specifically stated in the mark scheme, but should not be allowed if the difficulty level of the question has been lowered. *Either the correct response or an acceptable 'follow through' response should be marked as correct.*
There appears to be a misreading affecting the working.	This is when the pupil misreads the information given in the question and uses different information without altering the original intention or difficulty level of the question. For each misread that occurs, deduct one mark only.
The correct answer is in the wrong place.	Where a pupil has shown understanding of the question, the mark(s) should be given. In particular, where a word or number response is expected, a pupil may meet the requirement by annotating a graph or labelling a diagram elsewhere in the question.

The final answer is wrong but the correct answer is shown in the working.	Where appropriate, detailed guidance will be given in the mark scheme, and must be adhered to. If no guidance is given, markers will need to examine each case to decide whether:	
	the incorrect answer is due to a transcription error;	If so, award the mark.
	in questions not testing accuracy, the correct answer has been given but then rounded or truncated;	If so, award the mark.
	the pupil has continued to give redundant extra working which *does not* contradict work already done;	If so, award the mark.
	the pupil has continued to give redundant extra working which *does* contradict work already done.	If so, *do not* award the mark.
The pupil's answer is correct but the wrong working is seen.	A correct response should always be marked as correct unless the mark scheme states otherwise.	
The correct response has been crossed (or rubbed) out and not replaced.	Mark, according to the mark scheme, any legible crossed (or rubbed) out work that has not been replaced.	
More than one answer is given.	If all answers given are correct (or a range of answers are given, all of which are correct), the mark should be awarded unless prohibited by the mark scheme. *If both correct and incorrect responses are given no mark should be awarded.*	
The answer is correct but, in a later part of the question, the pupil has contradicted this response.	A mark given for one part should not be disallowed for working or answers given in a different part, unless the mark scheme specifically states otherwise.	

Marks			Correct response	Additional guidance
	1			**Carpets**
1m	a		Indicates 8 for first floor.	Accept correct number of tiles drawn in a correct arrangement if no numerical answer is given.

1m			Indicates 9 for second floor.	Accept any indication
				eg
				   2 × 4
				   3 by 3

1m	b		Indicates 80	
1m			Indicates the correct number of packs for the number of tiles indicated, provided the number of tiles indicated was over 10 eg • '8' for 80 tiles. • '9' for 81 tiles.	If no number of tiles is given, then accept 8 packs, but do not award the previous mark.
1m	c		Indicates 56	

1m			Indicates the correct number of packs for the number of tiles indicated, provided the number of tiles indicated was over 10 and not a multiple of 10
			eg
			• '6' for 56 tiles.
			• '7' for 64 tiles.
				If the pupil has already demonstrated, in part (b), the ability to find the correct number of packs for a number of tiles that is over 10 and not a multiple of 10, then allow follow through in part (c) for a number of tiles which is over 10 and is a multiple of 10
				eg
				   If '4' was accepted for 36 tiles in part (b), then accept '7' for 70 tiles for the second mark in part (c).
				
				If no number of tiles is given, then accept 6 packs, but do not award the previous mark.
				
				Ignore references to any number of tiles left over if the number of packs is correct
				eg, for 56 tiles
				   '6 boxes he'll have to chuck out 6.'
				
				Do not accept more or fewer than the correct number of packs
				eg
				   '5 packs plus 6 more tiles.'
				   'If she buys a dozen packs she'll be sure to have enough.'
				   '60'

Marks		Correct response	Additional guidance
	2		## Temperature
1m	a	Correctly indicates 24°C on the thermometer.	Drawings need not be accurate, as long as the pupil's intention is clear.
1m	b	Correctly indicates − 4°C on the thermometer.	Accept unlabelled or incorrectly labelled arrows or marks.
1m	c	Indicates 5	Accept any unambiguous indication eg 5 marked on the diagram

1m	d	Indicates the correct order for the temperatures
		eg
		• '− 10, − 1, 0, 3, 20'
			Accept any indication, as long as the order is correct
			eg
			    '10 −, − 1, 0, 3C, 20'
			    '− 10, 1, 0, 3, 20'
			    '− 10, − 1, − 0, .3, 20'
			    Arrows drawn from the temperatures to the correct positions.
			
			Accept a list of the correct positions for each temperature
			eg
			    '3 should be fourth, − 10 should be first,
			    0 should be third, 20 should be fifth, and
			    − 1 should be second.'
			    '4, 1, 3, 5, 2'
			
			Accept temperatures identified by their positions in the list given
			eg
			    'Second one should come first, then fifth, then third, then first, and the fourth one is the hottest.'
			    '2, 5, 3, 1, 4'

Marks		Correct response	Additional guidance
	3		## Pegs

1m	a	Draws a 9 by 2 rectangle.	Accept any indication of the correct rectangle eg
			
			    Corner pegs only shaded.
			    Line drawn around the pegs.
			    Line drawn through the pegs.

1m		Indicates 9 **and** indicates 2.	Accept length and width in either order. Accept responses based on rectangles formed with 18 pegs around the perimeter eg, for 2m **and** '8' pegs long '3' pegs wide
1m	b	Draws a row with a prime number of pegs greater than 5 **and** identifies the prime number of pegs drawn.	Acceptable numbers of pegs are: 7, 11, 13
1m	c	Explains why 9 is not a prime number eg <ul><li>'3 threes.'</li><li>'You can make a rectangle.'</li><li>'Three, three, three.'</li><li>'3 + 3 + 3'</li><li>'3 goes into 9.'</li><li>'It's the three times table.'</li><li>'A prime number only divides by itself.'</li><li>'9 splits into 3.'</li><li>'It's a square.'</li><li>Draws a 3 by 3 square.</li><li>'You can have 8 around the sides and one in the middle.'</li></ul>	**Do not accept** explanations which imply that only even numbers are not prime eg 'If it were even you could make a rectangle.'

Marks		Correct response	Additional guidance
	4		**Biscuits**

1m	a	Indicates 3	Accept any indication
			eg
			    '9 left.'
			    'Three out of the twelve.'
			    $\frac{3}{12}$
			
			Do not accept incorrect number of biscuits eaten
			eg
			    9

1m	b	Indicates $\frac{1}{2}$	Accept equivalent fractions, decimals, percentages, or correct fractions written as words
			eg
			    $\frac{6}{12}$
			    0.5
			    50%
			    'Half of them.'
			    'It's half and half.'
			    '2 quarters.'
			
			Do not accept fractions described by words
			eg
			    '6 out of 12'
			    '1 over 2'

1m	c	Indicates 15	**Allow follow through** from part (a), ie accept the difference between 18 and the number given in part (a).
			
			Do not accept incomplete or incorrect computations
			eg
			    9 + 6
			    9 + 6 = 14

Paper 1

Marks			Correct response	Additional guidance
	5			**Forty-five**
1m	a		Indicates, for the correct computation,	
			97	
1m			90	**Do not accept** 90%.
1m			10	
1m			180	
1m	b		Indicates, in the correct order, ÷ then +	Ignore partial working shown.

Paper 1

Marks		Correct response	Additional guidance
	6		**Number Lines**
1m	a	Indicates 50 eg • '50' • 'fifties' • '50s'	
1m	b	Indicates 80, 100, 120 in the correct order.	
1m	c	Indicates −10 in the correct position.	

1m		Indicates 0 and 10 in the correct positions.	Accept use of positive and negative signs with the 0
			eg
			  + 0
			  − 0

1m	d	Indicates −3 in the correct position.	
1m		Indicates 13 in the correct position **and** indicates steps of 4.	
1m	e	Indicates 7.9, 8(.0), 8.1 in the correct positions.	

1m		Indicates steps of 0.1
		eg
		• '0.1'
		• $\frac{1}{10}$
		• '0.1s'
		• 'tenths'
		• 'point 1'
			Do not accept incorrect or ambiguous responses
			eg
			  '1 decimal place'
			  'one decimal point'
			  '1 point'
			  '1 mm'

9

Paper 1

Marks		Correct response	Additional guidance
	7		**Symmetry**

1m	a	Indicates the correct pegs
		eg
		
			Shading need not be accurate as long as the pupil's intention is clear.
			
			Accept any indication of the correct pegs
			eg
			    Pegs circled.
			    Line drawn around the pegs.
			    Line drawn through the pegs.
			
			Do not accept more than the correct number of pegs indicated.

1m		Indicates the correct pegs eg 	

2m	b	**For 2m** indicates the correct pegs
		eg
		
		For only 1m indicates the correct pegs in any two of the three sections
		eg
		
			Shading need not be accurate as long as the pupil's intention is clear.
			
			Accept any indication of the correct pegs
			eg
			    Pegs circled.
			    Line drawn around the pegs.
			    Line drawn through the pegs.

Marks		Correct response	Additional guidance
	8		**Shading**
1m	a	Indicates the fraction is $\frac{3}{10}$	Accept equivalent fractions or decimal fractions, or correct fractions written as words eg 'Three tenths.'
1m		Indicates the percentage is 30	**Allow follow through** from an incorrect fraction, including rounding or truncation to the nearest integer. **Award only 1m** if both answers are correctly given but interchanged.
1m	b	Shades, or otherwise indicates, a total of 4 triangles.	Shading need not be accurate as long as the pupil's intention is clear.
1m		Indicates 40	**Allow follow through** from any incorrect shading other than 30%, 0% or 100%, or a value already credited in part (a).

Marks		Correct response	Additional guidance
	9		**Holding**

1m	a	Indicates a correct expression
		eg
		• '$n + 2$'
		• '$2 + n$'
			Accept letters other than n used.
			
			Accept multiplication by 1 or reversed notation for variables multiplied by a constant
			eg
			  '$2 + 1n$' for $2 + n$
			  '$n2$' for $2n$

1m	b	Indicates a correct expression eg • '$n - 1$' • '$-1 + n$'	Accept the word 'cubes' at the end of correct expressions. **Do not accept** other expressions with words.
1m	c	Indicates a correct expression eg • '$2n$' • '$2 \times n$' • '$n \times 2$' • '$n + n$'	Ignore a numerical substitution for n if a correct expression has been given. Otherwise, **do not accept** the inappropriate use of an = sign or incorrect attempts at simplification eg '$n = n + 2$' <u>'$n + 2 = 2n$'</u>

2m	d	**For 2m** explains there is a difference of one cube
		eg
		• 'One hand has one more cube than the other.'
		• 'One has one cube off. The other has two.'
		• 'In one hand it's –1, but the other is –2.'
		• 'One more in one hand.'
		• Draws a correct picture for each hand showing what is being held.
		or
		Indicates one is odd and one is even.
		or
		Indicates $2(n - 1) = 2n - 2$
		eg
		• 'In one hand it's $2n - 2$.'
		• 'No, $2(n - 1)$ means $n - 1$ then multiply by 2, so it's $- 2$.'
		
		For only 1m explains the difference in structure of the expressions without explaining the outcome
		eg
		• 'No, $2(n - 1)$ means $n - 1$ then multiply by 2.'
		• 'You do the brackets first so they're different.'
		• '$2n - 1$ means $2 \times n - 1$, $2(n - 1)$ means times everything by 2.'
		or
		Evaluates correctly both hands for one or more values of n.
			Award only 1m if a correct explanation is followed by incorrect algebra
			eg
			  'No, $2(n - 1) = 2n - 2$ but $2n - 1 = 1n$.'
			
			For 2m or 1m accept explanations where operations are given sequentially but without brackets
			eg, for 1m
			  'No because $2(n - 1)$ means $n - 1 \times 2$.'
			
			For 2m or 1m **do not accept** explanations which conclude that the expressions are the same.
			
			Do not accept a statement that they are different without justification
			eg
			  '$2n - 1$ is not the same as $2(n - 1)$'
			  'One of them has brackets.'
			  'More in first hand.'
			  'Brackets means times.'

Paper 1

Marks		Correct response	Additional guidance

			Outcomes
1m	a	Indicates $\frac{5}{9}$	Accept a correct probability written as an equivalent fraction, a decimal between 0.55 and 0.56 inclusive, or a percentage between 55% and 56% inclusive. Accept a correct probability accompanied by that probability written as words eg '$\frac{5}{9}$ that's 5 in 9' Otherwise, **do not accept** a probability written as words or as a ratio.
1m	b	Indicates $\frac{1}{3}$	Accept a correct probability written as an equivalent fraction, a decimal between 0.33 and 0.335 inclusive, or a percentage between 33% and 33.5% inclusive. Accept a correct probability accompanied by that probability written as words eg '1 out of 3 = 1 in 3 = 33%' If answers to both parts (a) and (b) use the correct digits but are expressed as words, this mark may be awarded eg '5 in 9' given in part (a) and '1 out of 3' given in part (b) is awarded 0 marks in part (a) and 1 mark in part (b). If answers to both parts (a) and (b) are expressed as correct percentages but the percentage signs are omitted, then award only the mark for part (b). **Do not accept** a probability written as a ratio.
1m	c	Shows all nine possible outcomes eg | x	2	3	4
2	4	6	8
3	6	9	12
4	8	12	16		Outcomes need not be in a table or be ordered in size.
1m		Completes the sentence correctly eg • Indicates a number greater than 12 but less than or equal to 16.	**Allow follow through** from incorrect outcomes.
1m		Completes the sentence correctly eg • Indicates a number that is 4 or less.	**Allow follow through** from incorrect outcomes.

13

Marks		Correct response	Additional guidance
	11		**Game**
1m	a	Indicates the card $n \div 2$	Throughout, **do not accept** letters other than n or N.
1m	b	Indicates the card n^2	
1m	c	Indicates the card $2n$	**Do not accept** cards not available eg
			$n \times 2$
1m		Indicates the card $n + n$	$n2$
1m	d	Indicates an expression equivalent to $3n + 2n$ eg	Accept multiplication by 1 or reversed notation for variables multiplied by a constant eg
		• '5n'	
		• 'n × 5'	$n5$
		• '8n − 3n'	$n2 + n3$
		• 'n + n + n + n + n'	$4n + 1n$
		• '2n + 3n'	
		• '3 × n + 2 × n'	

Marks		Correct response	Additional guidance
	12		**Numbers**
1m	a	Indicates 7 or +7	
1m 1m	b	Indicates – 8 as the card chosen. Gives a correct answer for their negative card eg • '–10' if – 8 chosen	**Allow follow through** from a negative number card, even if it is not one of the cards available. **Do not allow** follow through from a positive card. **Do not allow** follow through from 0, +0 or –0. If –10 is given as the answer but no card has been indicated, award only this second mark.
1m 1m		Indicates 9 or +9 as the card chosen. Gives a correct answer for their positive card eg • '–11' if 9 or +9 chosen	**Allow follow through** from a positive number card, even if it is not one of the cards available. If a negative number card has been chosen, **and** a positive number card has been chosen in the next section, **allow follow through** from any negative number card, even if it is not one of the cards available. **Do not allow** follow through from 0, +0 or –0. If –11 is given as the answer but no card has been indicated, award only this second mark.
1m 1m		Indicates – 8 as the card chosen. Gives a correct answer for their negative card eg • '6' or '+6' if – 8 chosen	**Allow follow through** from any negative number card, even if it is not one of the cards available. If a positive number card has been chosen, **and** a negative number card had been chosen in the previous section, **allow follow through** from any positive number card, even if it is not one of the cards available. **Do not allow** follow through from 0, +0 or –0. If 6 or +6 is given as the answer but no card has been indicated, award only this second mark.

Marks		Correct response	Additional guidance
	13		**Plants**

2m	a	**For 2m** indicates £33.25
		eg
		• '33.25'
		• '33.25p' on answer line.
		
		For only 1m shows a correct method with only one computational error
		eg
		• Shows 3325 with the decimal point omitted or incorrectly placed, or with units incorrectly stated.
		• Evaluates 35 × 5p and subtracts the answer from £35 making only one error throughout.
		• Shows in working 2850 and 475 (or 3150 and 175) incorrectly totalled with their answer correctly converted to pounds.
		or
		Shows a complete correct method with no errors but the total amount not found
		eg
		• Shows in working 2850 and 475 (or 3150 and 175) with the intention to add.
		• Shows in working 35 × £1 and 35 × 5p with the intention to subtract.
			For 2m accept 3325p elsewhere on page.
			
			For 2m do not accept 33.25p other than on the answer line.
			
			For 1m do not accept inconsistent units
			eg
			   '285 and 475'
			   '315 and 175'

2m	b	**For 2m** indicates 14
		
		For only 1m shows a complete correct method with no errors other than in the remainder, but the total number of trees is not stated
		eg
		• Shows 14 r 12 or 14.7...
		• Shows 14 and 238
		• Shows 15 and 255
		• Shows 17 × 10 = 170 and 17 × 4 = 68, with no ambiguity that these are the values chosen.
			Ignore reference to amount left over
			eg
			   '14, £12 left.'
			
			Ignore incorrect amount left over
			eg
			   '14, £7 left.'
			
			For 2m do not accept a remainder not given as an amount
			eg
			   '14 r 12'

Marks			Correct response	Additional guidance
	14			**Bath**

1m	a		States a possible reason for the reduced gradient eg
			 • 'The water is coming in more slowly.'
			 • 'Hot tap off.'
			 • 'Taps turning off.'
			 • 'One tap on.'
			 • 'Water pressure dropped.'
			 • 'The water is running out.'
			 • 'It's too hot so they're putting cold water in.'
			 • 'Bath gets wider.'
			 • 'Plug starts leaking.'
				Do not accept responses which indicate no flow eg
				    'The taps are turned off.'
				
				 Do not accept a description of the graph eg
				    'It gets less steep.'

1m	b		Indicates D to E.	Accept E to D.
1m	c		Indicates G to H.	Accept H to G.

Marks		Correct response	Additional guidance
	15		**Computer**
1m	a	Indicates $a = 100$ **and** $b = 140$	
1m		Indicates $c = 120$	**Allow follow through**, ie 360 – (angles a and b), provided angle c is given as greater than 90°.
1m	b	Indicates $d = 50$	
1m		Indicates $e = 130$	**Allow follow through**, ie 180 – angle d, provided angle e is given as greater than 90°.
1m	c	Indicates a correct value eg • '60' • '300'	Correct values include $360n \pm 60$, for any integer n.

Paper 1

Marks		Correct response	Additional guidance
	16		**Mean**
1m	a	Indicates 4	
2m	b	**For 2m** indicates 15 **For only 1m** shows in working a correct method with only one error or omission eg • Indicates the new total is 35 but omits or incorrectly calculates the number on the new card. • Incorrectly divides the total 20 to give an old mean of 4, then follows through correctly to give a new card of 10. • Indicates the number is old mean + (2 × 5).	**Award only 1m** if a pupil shows in working the correct value 15 but gives 7 as the answer.
1m	c	Indicates, in either order, 8 **and** 12.	

Marks		Correct response	Additional guidance
	17		**Octagon**
1m	a	Indicates $y = -10$	Accept equivalent equations. **Do not accept** responses not given as an equation.
1m	b	Indicates, in either order, A **and** B.	Accept any unambiguous indication of the correct line eg through '(0 , 15)' and '(15 , 0)'
1m	c	Indicates, on the diagram, the line $y = x$	Accept an unlabelled line only if no other lines have been drawn on the diagram. The line must meet or cross BA and EF. Accept a line which is not completely accurate as long as the pupil's intention is clear.

1m	d	Indicates a correct equation
		eg
		• ' $x = 0$ '
		• ' $y = 0$ '
		• ' $x = -y$ '
		• ' $y = -x$ '
		• ' $x + y = 0$ '
			Accept equivalent equations
			eg
			    $y = 0x$
			    $y = x \times 0$
			    $x = y - 2y$
			    $x = 10 - 10$
			
			Ignore the original line given alongside correct equations. Otherwise, **do not accept** a restatement of the original line, $y = x$
			
			Do not accept responses not given as an equation.

2m	e	**For 2m** indicates $x = 35$ and $y = 20$ **For only 1m** indicates either $x = 35$ **or** $y = 20$ **or** Shows a correct method to find both variables, making only one error.	
1m	f	Indicates (35, 20)	**Allow follow through** from part (e) for numerical values only. **Do not accept** unconventional notation eg $(x = 35, y = 20)$

Marks		Correct response	Additional guidance
	18	Marking overlay provided	**Sunshine**
1m	a	Indicates A	
2m	b	**For 2m** draws a line that is entirely within the solid lines on the marking overlay such that each end of this line goes beyond the broken line on the marking overlay **and** the line passes within 2mm of the intersection of the dashed lines for the means eg **For only 1m** draws a line that is entirely within the solid lines on the marking overlay such that each end of this line goes beyond the broken line but the line does not pass within 2mm of the intersection of the dashed lines for the means eg 	The line of best fit need not be straight. **Do not accept** a line of best fit which crosses either solid line on the marking overlay within or beyond either broken line eg **Do not accept** a line of best fit if either end of the line does not go beyond the broken line shown on marking overlay eg **Do not accept** more than one line of best fit drawn.
1m		Indicates a value between 400 and 520 inclusive eg • '450' • '500' • 'about 400'	Accept a range given provided it falls entirely within 400 to 520 inclusive eg 400 – 500

Marks		Correct response	Additional guidance
	19		**Operations**
1m	a	Indicates $0.8n$ only.	**For 2m or 1m** accept any indication of the correct card(s) eg 'Card 2' for $0.8n$

2m	b	**For 2m** indicates n^2, $\sqrt{n}$ and $\frac{1}{n}$ only.
		
		For only 1m indicates two of the three correct cards, and no other cards
		eg
		• 'n^2, $\sqrt{n}$'
		
		or
		
		Indicates the three correct cards, and one other card
		eg
		• 'n^2, $\sqrt{n}$, $\frac{n}{0.8}$, $\frac{1}{n}$'
			For 2m or 1m accept card(s) indicated where a value for n has been left inserted in the expression
			eg, for 2m
			  1^2, $\sqrt{1}$ and $\frac{1}{1}$ for part (b).
			  3.2, $\sqrt{4}$ and $\frac{1}{n}$ for part (c).
			
			eg, for 1m
			  0.8×4, $\sqrt{n}$ for part (c).
			  n^2, 0.4 and $\sqrt{\frac{1}{2}}$ for part (d).

2m	c	**For 2m** indicates $0.8n$, $\sqrt{n}$ and $\frac{1}{n}$ only. **For only 1m** indicates two of the three correct cards, and no other cards eg • '$0.8n$, $\sqrt{n}$' **or** Indicates the three correct cards, and one other card eg • '$0.8n$, $\sqrt{n}$, $\frac{n}{0.8}$, $\frac{1}{n}$'	
2m	d	**For 2m** indicates n^2 and $0.8n$ only. **For only 1m** indicates one of the two correct cards, and no other cards eg • '$0.8n$' **or** Indicates the two correct cards and one other card eg • 'n^2, $0.8n$, $\sqrt{n}$'	

Paper 1

Marks		Correct response	Additional guidance
			Tanks
	20		
1m	a	Indicates missing values for Capacity of bucket are 24 and 30	
1m		Indicates first two missing values for Number of buckets are 300 and 240	
1m		Indicates that missing value for Number of buckets corresponding to capacity of 15 is 160	
1m	b	Indicates an equation equivalent to T = BN or 2400 = BN eg • 'T = B × N' • 'B = $\frac{T}{N}$' • 'B × N = 2400' • 't = n × b = 2400'	**Do not accept** expressions eg BN **Do not accept** equations with words eg T = B times N T equals B × N **Do not accept** the use of letters other than those given in the question, apart from their lower case versions.
2m	c	**For 2m** indicates 5 hours 20 minutes. **For only 1m** shows required computation is 4000 divided by 12.5 (or any equivalent division). **or** Shows in working the value 320	It is not necessary for the computation to be attempted. For 1m **do not accept** attempts to multiply 12.5 by particular values to obtain 4000 unless the value 320 is shown.
1m	d	Indicates 2 hours 30 minutes.	Accept $2\frac{1}{2}$ hours or 150 minutes.
2m	e	**For 2m** indicates 3 hours 20 minutes. **For only 1m** shows a correct computation in working, or shows 3.33 or $3\frac{1}{3}$ in working but incorrectly converts this to hours and minutes eg • '$\frac{2}{3}$ × 5' • '5 ÷ 1.5' • '5 × $\frac{100}{150}$'	**For 2m** accept 200 minutes. **For 1m** accept a response given as 3 hours 33 minutes, or 3 hours 34 minutes, or $3\frac{1}{3}$ hours as evidence of correct working.
2m	f	**For 2m** indicates 10 hours. **For only 1m** shows in working that the given time is multiplied by 8 eg • '1hr 15 × 8' • '1.25 × 2 × 2 × 2' • '1.15 × 8'	**For 2m** accept 600 minutes. **For 1m** accept 9.2 or equivalent

Marks		Correct response	Additional guidance
	21	Marking overlay provided	**Farm**
1m	a	States a value between 30.50 and 32.00 inclusive eg • '31' • '31.11' • '32'	Accept a response given to one decimal place provided it is between 30.5 and 32.0 inclusive eg 31.5
1m	b	States a value between 82 and 87 inclusive eg • '85'	
1m	c	Shows on the grid vertical lines drawn down from the cumulative frequency graph at the points corresponding to cumulative frequency values of 10 (or 10.5 or 10.25) and 30 (or 30.5 or 30.75) to meet the horizontal axis. **or** Shows on horizontal axis points corresponding to cumulative frequency values of 10 (or 10.5 or 10.25) and 30 (or 30.5 or 30.75).	Horizontal lines need not be drawn across from the vertical axis at points 10 (or 10.5 or 10.25) and 30 (or 30.5 or 30.75) to meet the cumulative frequency graph. Ignore any lines drawn to find the median, and other lines drawn, provided it is clear that they do not relate to the interquartile range.
1m		Indicates a value between 9.50 and 11.50 inclusive.	**Do not accept** a range given eg 26 to 37

Marks		Correct response	Additional guidance

	21	Marking overlay provided	**Farm (cont)**
2m	d	**For 2m** draws a graph passing through the points (25,0), (30,1), (35,3), (40,6), (45,10), (50,20), (55,27) and (60,30)	The graph may be a curve or a series of straight lines. **Do not accept** two or more graphs drawn.

		For only 1m draws a graph passing through seven of the eight points
		eg
		• Graph passes through all eight points apart from (25,0)
		• Graph passes correctly through seven of the eight points but goes through (55,28) instead of (55,27)
			For 1m accept all eight points marked correctly but not all joined.
			
			For 1m accept graph drawn through all eight points consistently 1 square to the left of the correct positions [apart from (25,0)]
			ie
			    Graph passes through (24,0), (29,1), (34,3), etc.
			
			    Graph passes through (25,0), (29,1), (34,3), etc.
			
			Ignore additional points marked on the grid through which no graph is drawn.

1m	e	Indicates statement A is true and statements B and C are false.	**Do not allow** follow through from an incorrect graph drawn as the correct information is given in the tables.

Paper 1

Marks		Correct response	Additional guidance
	22		**Throw**
3m	a	**For 3m** indicates the correct value for c eg • '− 0.04' • '$\frac{-4}{100}$' • '$\frac{-2}{50}$' • '$\frac{-1}{25}$' **For only 2m** shows in working a correct equation of the form $a = bc$ where a and b are constants, in which no power is present eg • '− 4 = 100 × c' • '− 4 = c(100)' • '25c = − 1' **or** Shows in working that − 4 is divided by 100 eg • 'c → × 100 → + 6 → 2 − 0. 4 ← ÷ 100 ← − 6 ← 2' **For only 1m** shows in working that $(10 − x)^2$ when $x = 0$ simplifies to 100 eg • '2 = 6 + c100' • '2 = 6 +(100) × 6' **or** Correctly combines 2 and 6 into a single integer eg • '− 4 = c(10)²' • '4 = − 20c'	**For 3m** accept fractions with the − sign in the denominator eg $\frac{4}{-100}$ **For 2m** accept omission of the − sign eg 0.04 $\frac{4}{100}$ $\frac{2}{50}$ $\frac{1}{25}$

Marks			Correct response	Additional guidance

				Throw (cont)
	22			
3m	b		**For 3m** indicates 1.6	
			For only 2m shows in working that -0.1 is multiplied by -16 eg • $'-0.1\,(-16)'$	
			or	
			Indicates that the values of x^2 and $6x$ are both 0 eg • $'y = -0.1(0 - 0 - 16)'$	**For 2m** accept response given as -1.6
			For only 1m shows in working that $x = 0$ is substituted into $x^2 - 6x - 16$ eg • $'0^2 - 60 - 16'$	

Marks		Correct response	Additional guidance
	1		**Weather**
1m	a	Draws a bar to 25° for Friday. Draws a bar to 19° for Saturday. eg 	Bars need not be shaded, and drawings need not be accurate, as long as the pupil's intention is clear. The bar for Saturday must cover more than half of the 15° to 20° cell, but it must not touch the 20° line.
1m			
1m		Indicates a temperature between 26° and 28° inclusive.	

Paper 2

Marks		Correct response	Additional guidance

3m | b

For 3m makes all four correct connections
eg

For only 2m makes two or three correct connections.

For only 1m makes one correct connection.

Connecting lines need not touch either the speech bubble or the bar chart, as long as the pupil's intention is clear.

Do not accept more than one pupil connected to a bar chart, or more than one bar chart connected to a pupil
eg, for 2m, showing two correct connections

(Blank page)

Marks			Correct response	Additional guidance
	2			**Shapes**
1m	a		Indicates or	**Throughout**, shading or drawing need not be accurate, as long as the pupil's intention is clear. Accept correct shapes drawn on any grid. Ignore the shape given in the example, or individual single triangles, shaded or drawn on any grid.
1m	b		Indicates the correct shape not shaded in part (a).	Ignore a correct shape repeated on any grid.
1m	c		Indicates 4 triangles which form a bigger triangle similar to those forming the grid eg • •	
1m	d		Indicates 9 or more triangles which form a bigger triangle similar to those forming the grid eg • • •	

Marks		Correct response	Additional guidance
	3		**Cafe**

1m	a	Indicates £6.60
		eg
		• '6.60'
		• '6-60'
			Accept alternative unambiguous indications of the correct amount
			eg
			   6 60
			   £6.60p
			   6 pounds 60
			   6:60 pence
			
			Accept correct answer given in pence written elsewhere on the page, and not contradicted
			eg 660 pence
			
			Do not accept incorrect or ambiguous use of pounds or pence
			eg
			   £660 pence
			   660
			
			Do not accept incorrect placement of decimal points, spaces, etc, or incorrect use of 0
			eg
			   6.600
			   6.6
			   66 0
			   6-6-0

1m	b	Indicates £89.60
		eg
		• '89.60'
		• '89-60'
			Accept alternative unambiguous indications of the correct amount
			eg
			   £89.60 pence
			   89,60
			
			Accept correct answer given in pence written elsewhere on the page, and not contradicted
			eg
			   8960 p
			
			Do not accept incorrect or ambiguous use of pounds or pence
			eg
			   £8960
			
			Do not accept incorrect placement of decimal points, spaces, etc, or incorrect use of 0
			eg
			   8.960
			   89 600
			   89-6-0

1m		Indicates 5	

Marks		Correct response	Additional guidance
	4		**Distances**

1m	a	Indicates both Bangor **and** Hull.	Accept any indication of the two towns
			eg
			    'H and B'
			    Arrows drawn to the two place names.
			
			Do not accept responses which mention only the distance, with no indication of the two towns
			eg
			    199

1m	b	Indicates 289	
1m		Indicates 248	
1m		Indicates 537	**Allow follow through** from the first two responses only if both numbers have at least three digits.

Paper 2

Marks		Correct response	Additional guidance
	5		**Spiral**
1m	a	Draws the next 4 lines correctly.	The fourth line must have an intended length of six units. Ignore any continuation of the spiral beyond the four lines required. Lines need not be completely accurate, nor drawn with a ruler, as long as the pupil's intention is clear.
1m	b	Indicates 12	
1m	c	Indicates the correct rule eg • ' ÷ 2' • 'Divide by 2' • 'Half of it.' • ' × $\frac{1}{2}$ '	**Do not accept** the value 2 or $\frac{1}{2}$ without the correct operation indicated.
1m	d	Indicates 9	**Allow follow through** from an incorrect rule given in part (c).

Marks		Correct response	Additional guidance
	6		**Packs**
1m	a	Indicates 20	
1m		Indicates 120	**Allow follow through** for previous response correctly multiplied by 6.
1m	b	Indicates 90	
1m	c	Indicates any two positive integers which multiply together to make 12.	

Marks		Correct response	Additional guidance

	7		**Chains**

1m	a	Indicates a correct rule
		eg
		• '× 2'
		• 'Doubles.'
		• 'Add on the number you're at.'
		• '2 + 2, 4 + 4, 8 + 8'
		• 'Go up 2, then 4, then 8'
		• 'It's 2, then 2 × 2, then 2 × 2 × 2'
			Do not accept an incorrect statement
			eg
			    'Go up in twos.'
			
			Where a rule is explained as a progression, **do not accept** fewer than 3 differences specified
			eg
			    '+2 , + 4'

3m	b	1m for each different stated rule accompanied by the correctly continued chain. Examples of correct chains and rules include:
		
		those with a constant term to term rule
		eg
		• '1 , 5 , 9 , 13 , 17 ... add 4'
		
		• '1 , 5 , 25 , 125 , 625 ... × 5'
		
		• '1 , 5 , 21 , 85 , 341 ... × 4 + 1'
		
		• '1 , 5 , 17 , 53 , 161 ... × 3 + 2'
		
		• '1 , 5 , 13 , 29 , 61 ... × 2 + 3'
		
		• '1 , 5 , 29 , 173 , 1037 ... × 6 – 1'
		
		those with a constant multi-part term to term rule
		eg
		• '1 , 5 , 8 , 12 , 15 ... + 4, + 3'
		
		• '1 , 5 , 1 , 5 , 1 ... forward 4, backward 4'
		
		those described by changing differences
		eg
		• '1 , 5 , 11 , 19 , 29 ... + 4, + 6, + 8, + 10'
		
		• '1 , 5 , 8 , 10 , 11 ... + 4, + 3, + 2'
		
		• '1 , 5 , 10 , 16 , 23 ... it's 1 more each time.'
		
		those with a Fibonacci-type pattern
		eg
		• '1 , 5 , 6 , 11 , 17 ... add first 2, then next 2, then the next 2'
		
		• '1 , 5 , 5 , 25 , 125 ... multiply each number by the number before.'
		
		those which describe the numbers in the chain
		eg
		• '1 , 5 , 9 , 13 , 17 ... every other odd number.'
			Each rule must give sufficient information to enable the chain to be continued.
			
			Accept more sophisticated rules such as the nth term given
			eg
			    '1 , 5 , 9 , 13 , 17 ... $4n - 3$'
			
			Do not accept a rule which ignores the value 1 and uses the 5 as the first number in the chain.
			
			Do not accept errors or omissions in generating the numbers; a calculator is available.
			
			Do not accept a rule which is similar to one already credited
			eg
			    '+ 4' and '+ 5 – 1'
			
			Do not accept a rule which is not quantified
			eg
			    '1 , 5 , 10 , 16 , 23 ... add more each time.'
			    '1 , 5 , 1 , 5 , 1 ... go forwards then backwards.'
			
			Where a rule is explained by listing changing differences, **do not accept** fewer than 3 differences specified
			eg
			    '1 , 5 , 8 , 10 , 11 ... + 4, + 3'
			
			Do not accept rules which reach a particular term and then remain constant
			eg
			    '1 , 5 , 5 , 5 , 5 ... don't go higher than 5'

Paper 2

Marks		Correct response	Additional guidance
	8		**Cards**
1m	a	Gives a correct explanation eg • '4 of each.' • 'Equal chances.' • 'Half are triangles.' • 'Just as likely.' • 'Fifty fifty.' • 'Evens.' • 'Not more ■.'	Throughout, accept unconventional names for ■ and △ as long as the pupil's intention is clear. **Do not accept** explanations which imply the likelihood cannot be found eg 'No-one knows what she'll get - he's just guessing.'
1m		Indicates certain.	Accept equivalent words or phrases.
1m		Indicates likely.	Accept equivalent words or phrases.
1m	b	Completes the sentence correctly eg • '(any number) than ■' • '(any number) than △' • '△ than ■' • '(any number other than 9) than 9' • 'Even than odd.' • 'White than black.' • 'Lower number than higher number.'	The second entry must be true for the cards shown in the question. The first entry may refer to cards which are not shown in the question.
1m		Ticks the "higher than 5" box **and** justifies the decision eg • '4 higher, 3 lower.' • '8, 9, 7 and 9 are bigger.' • 'Only 3 smaller.' • 'More higher.' • 'Not many lower.' • 'It's 4 out of 7.' • '4 in 7 higher, 3 in 7 lower.'	Accept no box ticked only if the justification makes it clear that "higher than 5" is intended. **Do not accept** responses which do not give a justification eg 'It's a higher chance.' 'The probability of higher than 5 is more.' **Do not accept** justifications which do not refer, explicitly or implicitly, to all the cards eg 'Higher, there are two 9s.' If justifications are quantified, then **do not accept** incorrect quantification eg '5 cards higher, 3 lower.' 'It's $\frac{4}{8}$ not $\frac{3}{8}$'

36

Marks		Correct response	Additional guidance
	9		**Child**
1m	a	Indicates 48	Accept change of units provided correct units are indicated eg 0.48m
1m	b	Indicates 3.8	Accept equivalent decimals or fractions. Accept change of units provided correct units are indicated eg 3kg 800g
1m	c	Indicates 103	**Do not accept** incomplete or incorrect computations eg 100 + 3

Marks		Correct response	Additional guidance
			Playgroup
1m	a	Indicates 20	**Do not accept** a value given as a percentage.
1m		Indicates 40	**Allow follow through** from an incorrect number of girls, provided the percentage given is greater than 0 and less than 50.
2m	b	**For 2m** draws all 3 sections correctly eg **For only 1m** shows 3 sections totalling 100% **and** draws correctly one section but with no two sections the same size.	**For 2m** accept incorrect or omitted labels.
1m		Labels each section correctly with the ages eg • '4, 3, 2'	**Allow follow through** from an incorrect drawing only if no sections are the same size, and 4 years is the largest labelled section and 2 years is the smallest labelled section. Accept additional correct information given as long as there are correct labels for the ages.

Marks		Correct response	Additional guidance
	11	Marking overlay provided	**Shell**
3m	a	**1m** for indicating each correct position eg	Accept any unambiguous indication of where the square should be. **Do not accept** more than one square indicated on any diagram unless it is clearly shown that multiple responses are intended eg, accept
1m	b	Draws a rectangle which fits along the upper horizontal edge given **and** draws two correctly oriented right-angled triangles which fit along vertical edges given eg, one of	For this mark the drawing need not be accurate as long as the pupil's intention is clear. Accept the rectangle drawn as a square. Accept tabs drawn, otherwise **do not accept** extra shapes.
1m		Draws a 5.7cm by 4cm rectangle within the accuracy as specified by the overlay.	This mark is available for an accurately drawn rectangle anywhere on the page.
1m		Draws two right-angled triangles within the accuracy as specified by the overlay.	This mark is available for two accurately drawn triangles anywhere on the page.

Marks		Correct response	Additional guidance
	12		**Driving**
1m	a	Indicates 80	
1m	b	Indicates a value between 53 and 57 inclusive.	
1m	c	Indicates a value between 14 and 16 inclusive.	
2m	d	**For 2m** indicates 10 **For only 1m** shows the value 60	

	13	Marking Overlay Provided	**Sector**
1m		Draws one edge of 8.5cm ± 2mm.	Accept the end of a line defined by the intersection of the line with the arc or the other line.
1m		Draws the second edge of 8.5cm ± 2mm.	
1m		Draws an angle of 74° ± 2°	
1m		Draws a correct arc, with radius 8.5cm ± 2mm, with the centre at the apex of the drawing.	**Allow follow through** from an incorrect angle. Ignore continuation of the arc beyond the lines.

	14		**Toys**
1m	a	Indicates 106.25	Accept £106.25p or other non-ambiguous indication of cost such as 10625p written other than on the given answer line.
1m	b	Indicates 40	

1m	c	Indicates excellent **and** not boxed
		 eg
		 • 'Excellent. No.'
		 • 'Best but isn't.'
			Accept unambiguous responses
			 eg
			    65%
			
			 Do not accept partial responses
			 eg
			    'Excellent.'

Marks		Correct response	Additional guidance
	15		**Survey**
1m	a	Indicates overlap exists eg • 'You can tick 2 boxes.' • 'Where does a 40 year old tick?' • 'It should be 31 to 39' • 'Some numbers used twice.'	Ignore any boxes ticked. Ignore responses which imply a wider age range is required, or that it is impolite to ask ages.
2m	b	**For 2m** indicates two or more labels that cover all possible prices with no overlaps and no gaps eg • 'Less than £1; £1 - £2; more than £2' • 'More than £2.50; less than or equal to £2.50' • '51p - £2; 1p - 50p; nothing; other.' **For only 1m** indicates two or more labels that cover some possible price intervals eg • '£2 to £3; £3+; nothing.' • 'More than £2.50; less than £2.50' • 'Less than £1; less than £5; less than £6.' • '£1 - £2; £4 - £7; £7 or more.'	Ignore any boxes ticked. Ignore up to two categories left blank. **For 2m or 1m** accept unrealistic prices eg, for 2m 'Less than £20; £20 - £50; more than £50.' For 2m or 1m **do not accept** responses unless at least two labels refer to specific price intervals rather than 'nothing', 'other', etc.

Marks		Correct response	Additional guidance

	15		**Survey (cont)**
1m	c	States one valid disadvantage. Possible responses include reference to: the limited age group eg • 'Same age.' • 'Older people won't be asked.' • 'It won't vary much.' • 'Not representative.' pupils not being the purchasers eg • 'They won't know the price.' • 'They don't do the shopping.' • 'Pupils don't buy the biscuits themselves.' • 'They don't have enough money.' the validity of the responses eg • 'They won't take it seriously.' • 'They'll only ask their friends.' • 'Might lie.' inconvenience eg • 'It will disrupt lessons.'	Ignore irrelevant or incorrect statements given alongside correct statements. **Do not accept** statements with no explanation of why it is a disadvantage eg 'It's not fair.' 'It wouldn't be easy.' **Do not accept** statements that imply sampling is unfair eg 'They're only asking some of the pupils not all of them.'
1m	d	States one valid advantage. Possible responses include reference to: the ease of administration eg • 'Quick.' • 'Easy to find 50 people.' • 'You can get the questionnaires back.' • 'Safer.' the detailed profile of one age group eg • 'They'll know exactly what children like.' • 'They'll know whether to sell them in school.' • 'School has a variety of types of pupils.' the validity of the responses eg • 'His friends will tell the truth.' • 'They'll be interested.'	Ignore irrelevant or incorrect statements given alongside correct statements. **Do not accept** statements with no explanation of why it is an advantage eg 'They are all about the same age.' 'It's fair.' 'Easy.' 'Children like biscuits.' **Do not accept** statements which restate the purpose of the survey eg 'They can tell you what they think.'

Marks		Correct response	Additional guidance
	16	Marking overlay provided	**Drawing**
2m	a	**For 2m** makes a correct drawing eg **For only 1m** draws a diagram as above with two squares adjacent and only one 1 by 2 rectangle added or omitted. **or** Shows the complete drawing as 2 by 10, with missing or extra fold lines.	The drawing need not be accurate as long as the pupil's intention is clear. Indication of dimensions is not required.
3m	b	**For 3m** draws the prism correctly eg **For only 2m** draws the L shaped face with the correct outline even if remaining faces are incorrect, missing or have redundant lines eg **For only 1m** draws a complete prism, using the isometric paper correctly, that is 2 cubes high or 2 cubes wide, provided it is not a cuboid or an exact copy of a diagram given earlier in the question. **or** Draws the L shaped face in the correct shape but does not use isometric paper eg 	The drawing need not be accurate as long as the pupil's intention is clear. Accept any correct orientation. A complete set of all orientations is shown on the overlay, with the 'top' face shaded. **For 3m, 2m or 1m** accept drawings showing the prism with some or all of the lines partitioning the faces not shown eg for 3m for 3m **For 3m, 2m or 1m** accept enlargements of the prism.

Marks		Correct response	Additional guidance
	17		**Walls**

1m	a	Indicates a correct simplified expression
		eg
		• '$m + 2n + p$'
		• '$n \times 2 + m + p$'
			Accept multiplication by 1 or 0
			eg
			    '$1m$' for m
			    '$0t$' for 0

1m
 	
1m
 	
1m
 	
1m
	b	Indicates a correct simplified expression for:
		the left brick
		eg
		• '$2h - 1$'
		• '$-1 + 2 \times h$'
		the right brick
		eg
		• '$2h$'
		• '$2 \times h$'
		
		Indicates a correct simplified expression for:
		the top brick
		eg
		• '$8u$'
		• '$u \times 8$'
		the lower brick
		eg
		• '$3t + 4u$'
		• '$u \times 4 + 3 \times t$'
			Accept reversed notation for variables multiplied by a constant
			eg
			    '$u8$' for $8u$
			
			Do not accept unsimplified expressions
			eg
			    '$8u + 3t - 3t$' for $8u$
			
			Do not accept incorrect letters given, other than their upper case versions.

2m	c	**For 2m** indicates a valid reason with reference made, directly or indirectly, to j
		eg
		• 'The top is $2h + 2j + 2k$. Each one is even.'
		• (Wall completed correctly) 'Everything is $\times 2$'
		• 'j gets used twice, the others are already even.'
		• Shows $2h + 2j + 2k = 2(h + j + k)$.
		• 'If j is odd, it's odd and odd on the second row, and two odds make an even. If j is even, it stays even all the way up.'
		• 'Second row must be 2 evens or 2 odds. Then two evens make an even, so do two odds.'
		
		For only 1m gives a partial explanation with reference made, directly or indirectly, to j
		eg
		• 'If they're all even, it goes even all the way up. If they're all odd, the top is still even.' (mixture of odds and evens not considered)
		• 'There will be two js.'
		• 'Second row must be 2 evens or 2 odds.'
		or
		Shows through accurate numerical substitution that an even number is obtained for the top brick.
			For 2m or 1m if the wall is completed, the expressions should be correct.
			
			For 2m or 1m do not accept statements without justification. It is not sufficient to see the wall correctly completed to $2h + 2j + 2k$, or a statement that $2h + 2j + 2k$ is even.
			
			For 2m or 1m do not accept statements which do not refer directly or indirectly to j
			eg
			    '$h + k$ are multiplied by 2 so it's even.'
			    'Any combination of odds and evens will be even at the top.'

Paper 2

Marks		Correct response	Additional guidance
	18		**Hands**
2m	a	**For 2m** indicates 48.039... rounded or truncated to 2 or more significant figures eg • '48%'	Throughout, **do not accept** computations based upon the incorrect selection of data.
		For only 1m shows in working 196 ÷ 408, or (28 + 168) ÷ 408, or equivalent.	It is not enough to see 196 and 408. Some indication must be given as to how these numbers should be processed.
2m	b	**For 2m** indicates a correct ratio eg • '1 : 5.8' • '1 to 5.8'	Accept 5.8 written as an equivalent decimal or fraction. Accept an answer written on the dotted line. Accept 1 : 6 given as the ratio only if 5.8, or 60 and 348, are shown in the working.
		For only 1m gives correct ratio in a different form eg • '5 : 29' • '30 to 174' • '0.17 : 1' • '60 : 348' • '$\frac{60}{348}$' **or** Shows in working a correct method eg • '348 ÷ 60' • '(180 + 168) ÷ (32 + 28)'	**For 1m** accept 1 : 5 given as the ratio only if 5.8, or 60 and 348, are shown in the working. Otherwise, for 1m **do not accept** responses which do not indicate how the numbers 60 and 348 should be processed.
1m	c	Indicates the correct probability eg • '0.44117' • '0.44' • '44%' • '$\frac{180}{408}$'	Accept the probability written as a decimal, fraction or percentage only. Accept decimals and percentages rounded or truncated to two or more significant figures, or fractions which are equivalent to these. Accept a correct probability seen which has then been incorrectly cancelled. Equivalent fractions include $\frac{90}{204}$; $\frac{45}{102}$; $\frac{60}{136}$; $\frac{30}{68}$; $\frac{15}{34}$

44

Marks			Correct response	Additional guidance

	19			**Triangle**
3m			**For 3m** indicates 84 or 84.0	For 3m, 2m or 1m **do not accept** any value found through scale drawing.
			For only 2m indicates the height of the triangle is 24	**Award 2m** for values such as 84.00, 84.000 etc.
			or	
			Uses trigonometry, or other appropriate method, to obtain an area in the range 83.6 to 84.4 inclusive (other than 84 or 84.0).	
			or	
			Shows in working the correct use of Pythagoras' theorem, or other appropriate method, with only one numerical error **and** correctly follows through from their incorrect height to find an area.	**For 2m** correct use of Pythagoras' theorem must include evidence, directly or indirectly, of the intent to subtract 7^2 from 25^2.
			For only 1m shows in working the intent to use Pythagoras' theorem, or other equivalent method.	**For 1m** sufficient evidence to indicate the intent to use Pythagoras' theorem includes 25^2 (or 625) $\pm$ 7^2 (or 49). The use of $a^2 + b^2 = c^2$ without numerical substitution would not be sufficient.

Paper 2

Marks		Correct response	Additional guidance
	20 .	Marking overlay provided	**Tree**
1m	a	Draws a straight line parallel to edge of school buildings and 6cm ± 2mm away from it.	Accept drawing of only part of this line provided it meets the fence at the bottom of plan and meets the line representing 10m from the centre of the pond. Accept a straight line or a freehand line drawn that lies entirely within the lines on the marking overlay.
1m		Draws an arc of a circle with centre the middle of the pond and radius 5cm ± 2mm.	The arc of a circle must at least meet the fence at the bottom of plan and meet the line representing 12m from the school buildings. Accept an arc or a freehand arc drawn that lies entirely within the lines on the marking overlay.
1m		Indicates all the region(s) inside the fence, outside the line representing 10m from the centre of the pond and outside the line representing 12m from the school buildings. **or** Indicates only the region at the bottom of the plan if two possible regions have been formed from lines drawn within the tolerance lines on the marking overlay.	**Allow follow through** from incorrect lines that have been drawn. **Do not accept** indication of a region that is bounded by 4 or more straight lines, other than a region that extends across the garden from one part of the fence to the other (see opposite page for further clarification). **Do not accept** indication of one precise location for the tree. **Do not accept** a region that does not have part of the fence as one of its boundary lines. **Do not accept** an explanation that there is nowhere the tree can be planted.
2m	b	**For 2m** indicates a value between 15.7(0) and 15.71 inclusive, or 5π eg • '15.7' • '15.707963' **For only 1m** shows in working that the area of the path and pond is a value that rounds to 28.3, or is 9π eg • '28.26' shown in working.	**For 2m** accept a response given as 15.5 or 16 provided a value between 15.7(0) and 15.71 inclusive is shown in working. **For 1m** accept a response given as 15.5 or 16 without a value between 15.7(0) and 15.71 inclusive shown in working. **For 1m** accept a response given as 15 provided a value between 15.7(0) and 15.71 inclusive is shown in working.

Tree Part (a) Third Mark

Award 1m for a region that is bounded by 4 or more straight lines if it is bounded on the **left** by the line representing 12m from the school buildings

eg

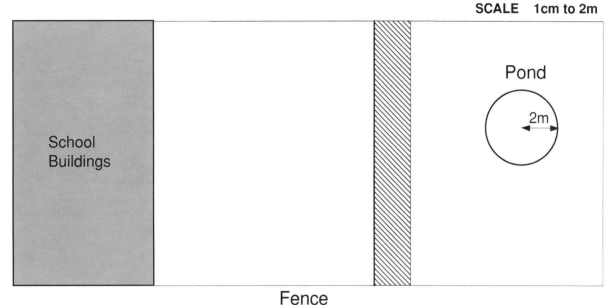

Do not accept a region that is bounded by 4 or more straight lines if it is bounded on the **right** by the line representing 12m from the school buildings

eg

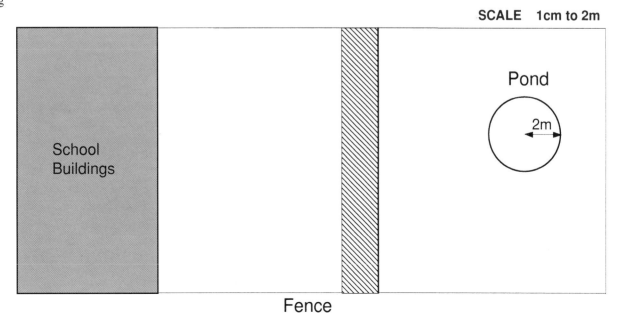

Marks		Correct response	Additional guidance
	21		**Cereal**
2m	a	**For 2m** indicates 9.26 or 9.3 **For only 1m** shows in working the values 264, 220, 210 and 102, but incorrectly adds these together with the 130. **or** Shows in working three of the values 264, 220, 210, and 102, and correctly adds the four given values together with the 130.	**For 2m** accept a response given as 9 provided 9.26, 926 or 9.3 is shown in working. **For 2m** accept a response given as 9.2 provided 9.26 or 926 is shown in working. **For 1m** accept 926 shown in working.
2m	b	**For 2m** indicates a value between 9 and 12 inclusive eg • '12' **For only 1m** indicates a value between 8 and 14 inclusive but not between 9 and 12 inclusive eg • '$8\frac{1}{2}$'	**For 2m or 1m** accept responses involving fractions or decimals eg, for 2m 10.08

1m	c	Indicates chart B (or Raisins)
		and
		indicates that the range covers 6 to 30, or is 24
		eg
		• 'Raisins go from 6 to 30.'
		• 'B has a range of 24.'
			Accept responses which explain how to find the range, but do not do not specify its value
			eg
			  'Chart B because the difference between the highest and lowest number of raisins is bigger.'
			
			Accept responses in which Chart B (or Raisins) is not specified, provided it is clear from the explanation that it has the greater range
			eg
			  '30 − 6 > 18 − 4'
			  '24 is more'
			  '6 - 30 is greater than 4 - 18'
			
			Do not accept responses that refer only to the upper value of the range, or to the range of one or more bars
			eg
			  'Raisins because it goes up to 30'
			  'B, the number of raisins is from 6 − 10 to 26 − 30'
			
			Do not accept responses in which Chart B is indicated but the explanation repeats or rephrases the question
			eg
			  'B as it has the biggest range of numbers.'
			  'Chart B has greater variation.'

Marks		Correct response	Additional guidance
	21		**Cereal** (cont)

1m	d	Indicates the correct probability as a fraction, decimal or percentage equivalent to 0.59 or 0.6
		eg
		• '0.59'
		• '0.6'
		• $\frac{59}{100}$
		• '60%'
			Do not accept ratios, probabilities written in words or fractions in which one or both numbers involve decimals
			eg
			  59 : 100
			  59 out of 100
			  6 in 10
			  $\frac{5.9}{10}$

2m	e	**For 2m** indicates the correct probability as a fraction, decimal or percentage
		eg
		• $\frac{138}{10000}$
		• '0.0138'
		• $\frac{69}{5000}$
		• '1.38%'
		
		For only 1m shows in working that the probability is $\frac{6}{100} \times \frac{23}{100}$ or 0.06 × 0.23
		
		or
		
		Shows in working 138 and 10000, or equivalent
		eg
		• '138 out of 10000'
		• '138 : 10000'
			For 2m **do not accept** probabilities written in words.
			eg
			  138 out of 10000
			
			For 1m accept a response given as a fraction in which one or both numbers involve decimals
			eg
			  $\frac{1.38}{100}$
			
			For 1m accept the correct ratio
			eg
			  138 : 9862
			  69 : 4931

Marks		Correct response	Additional guidance

<table>
<tr><td></td><td>22</td><td></td><td>Compactness</td></tr>
<tr>
<td>3m</td>
<td>a</td>
<td>

For 3m indicates a value between 0.63 and 0.65 inclusive, or $\dfrac{2}{\pi}$, or equivalent fraction, without any scale drawing used.

For only 2m shows in working $\dfrac{4 \times 36}{\pi \times 72}$ or $\dfrac{144}{\pi \times 72}$ or $\dfrac{4 \times 36}{a}$ or $\dfrac{144}{a}$ where a is a value between 222 and 228 inclusive, without any scale drawing used.

or

Shows in working that $K^2 = 2A$
eg
• '4 triangles make 2 squares' with sketch:

For only 1m shows in working 72 or $\sqrt{72}$, or a value between 8.4 and 8.5 inclusive, or a value between 70.5 and 72.3 inclusive, without any scale drawing used.

</td>
<td>

Throughout, accept a value between 3.1(0) and 3.15 inclusive used for π in numerical expressions.

If a scale drawing has been used to find a correct value for K, then **only 1m** may be awarded.

For 3m accept 0.6 or 0.7 with a value between 0.63 and 0.65 inclusive shown in working.

For 2m accept $\dfrac{4 \times 36}{\pi \times x^2}$ or $\dfrac{144}{\pi \times x^2}$ where x is a value between 8.4 and 8.5 inclusive.

or

$\dfrac{4 \times 36}{\pi \times y}$ or $\dfrac{144}{\pi \times y}$ where y is a value between 70.5 and 72.3 inclusive.

or

Indicates a value between 0.7(0) and 0.72 inclusive, or $\dfrac{9}{4\pi}$

For 1m accept $\dfrac{4 \times 36}{\pi \times x^2}$ or $\dfrac{144}{\pi \times x^2}$ shown in working where x is a value outside the range 8.4 to 8.5 inclusive.

or

$\dfrac{4 \times 36}{\pi \times y}$ or $\dfrac{144}{\pi \times y}$ where y is a value outside the range 70.5 to 72.3 inclusive
eg
$$\dfrac{4 \times 36}{\pi \times 36}$$

For 1m accept a value between 0.63 and 0.65 inclusive, or $\dfrac{2}{\pi}$, or equivalent fraction, but where a scale drawing has been used to find the value of K.

</td>
</tr>
</table>

Marks		Correct response	Additional guidance
	22		**Compactness** (cont)
2m	b	**For 2m** indicates a value between 0.52 and 0.54 inclusive, or $\frac{480}{289\pi}$, or equivalent fraction, without any scale drawing used.	If a scale drawing has been used to find a correct value for K, then **only 1m** may be awarded **For 2m** accept 0.5 with a value between 0.52 and 0.54 inclusive shown in working.
		For only 1m shows in working 289 or $\sqrt{289}$, or a value between 16.98 and 17.02 inclusive, or a value between 288.3 and 289.7 inclusive, without any scale drawing used.	**For 1m** accept a value between 0.52 and 0.54 inclusive, or $\frac{480}{289\pi}$, or equivalent fraction, but where a scale drawing has been used to find the value of K.
3m	c	**For 3m** indicates a value between 0.35 and 0.38 inclusive, or $\frac{2}{\sqrt{3}\pi}$, or equivalent fraction, without any scale drawing used	If a scale drawing has been used, then **only 1m** may be awarded. **For 3m** accept 0.3 or 0.4 with a value between 0.35 and 0.38 inclusive shown in working.
		For only 2m shows in working that the area of the rhombus is a value between 28 and 29 inclusive, or that the value of 4A is between 112 and 116 inclusive, without any scale drawing used. eg • 28.87 shown in working	
		For only 1m shows in working that $\tan 30° = \frac{x}{5}$ or $\tan 60° = \frac{5}{x}$, or an equivalent trigonometric expression involving tan eg • $\tan 30° = \frac{AB}{5}$ shown in working. • $5 \times \tan 30°$ shown in working. • 2.89 shown in working.	**For 1m** accept a value between 0.57 and 0.58 inclusive used for tan 30°, or a value between 1.73 and 1.74 inclusive used for tan 60°, in calculation eg $\quad$ 0.5774 × 5 shown in working. **For 1m** accept a value between 0.35 and 0.38 inclusive, or equivalent fraction, but where a scale drawing has been used.
2m	d	**For 2m** indicates 1 **For only 1m** shows in working 36π or a value that rounds to 113	
1m	e	Indicates 1 **or** Indicates response given to part (d). **or** Explains that all circles have the same compactness value, or that similar shapes have the same compactness value.	

Paper 2

Marks		Correct response	Additional guidance
	23		**Bus**

1m	a	Describes Bus A and Bus B passing each other in opposite directions, or implies opposite directions
		eg
		• 'They drive past each other in different directions.'
		• 'Bus B is still going to the Red Lion, Bus A is coming back.'
		• 'They passed each other.'
			Do not accept false explanations or explanations that do not state or imply opposite directions
			eg
			    'Bus B passed Bus A.'
			    'Bus A was coming down the hill, Bus B going up it.'
			    'They are in the same place at the same time.'
			    'They meet.'
			    'The buses cross paths.'
			    'Bus A crashes into B.'

1m	b	Describes Bus A passing Bus B while Bus B has stopped eg • 'A went past B while B was not moving.' • 'Bus A overtakes Bus B at a bus stop.'	**Do not accept** explanations which do not state or imply that Bus B has stopped eg 'Bus A went past Bus B.'
1m	c	Indicates a value between 17 and 18 inclusive eg • '17.777777' • '17.8'	

Paper 2

Marks	Correct response	Additional guidance

	23		**Bus (cont)**
2m	d	**For 2m** indicates a value between 28.2 and 28.3 inclusive eg • '28.24' **For only 1m** shows in working the computation $8 \times \frac{60}{17}$, or equivalent eg • ' $\frac{60}{17} \times 8$ ' • '$8 \div \frac{17}{60}$' • '$8 \div 17 \times 60$'	**For 2m** accept response given as 28 provided a value between 28.2 and 28.3 inclusive is shown in working. Accept a value between 3.52 and 3.53 inclusive for $\frac{60}{17}$, or a value between 0.28 and 0.29 inclusive for $\frac{17}{60}$ eg 8×3.53 $8 \div 0.28$
2m	e	**For 2m** indicates a value between 13.3 and 13.6 inclusive. **For only 1m** indicates a value between 12.2 and 14.3 inclusive but not between 13.3 and 13.6 inclusive. **or** Shows in working the computation $21.5 \times \frac{5}{8}$, or equivalent eg • '$21.5 \times 5 \div 8$' • '$\frac{21.5}{8} \times 5$' • '$21.5 \times \frac{5}{8}$'	Accept a value between 0.62 and 0.63 inclusive for $\frac{5}{8}$, or 1.6 for $\frac{8}{5}$ eg 21.5×0.62 $21.5 \div 1.6$

Paper 2

Marks		Correct response	Additional guidance
	24		**Storm**

2m	a	**For 2m** indicates a value in standard form between 2.9×10^5 and 3.2×10^5 inclusive
		eg
		• '3.055×10^5'
		• '3.1×10^5'
		
		For only 1m indicates a correct value between 290000 and 320000 not in standard form
		eg
		• '0.0003055×10^9'
		• '305500'
		• '305555.56'
			For 1m accept a response using the E notation with a value between 2.9 and 3.2 inclusive
			eg
			    3.055 E 5
			or
			Accept a response involving a value between 2.9 and 3.2 inclusive with $(+)5$ or $(+)05$
			eg
			    3.1^5

2m	b	**For 2m** indicates a value in standard form as $x \times 10^5$ where x is a value between 8.4 and 9.9 inclusive with no non-zero digits given for thousandths and below.
		or
		Indicates $1(.0) \times 10^6$, or 10^6
		or
		Indicates a value as a number between 840000 and 1000000 inclusive with no non-zero digits given for hundreds and below
		eg
		• '9.17×10^5'
		• '1.0×10^6'
		• '917000'
		• '1000000'
		
		For only 1m indicates a value in standard form as $x \times 10^5$ where x is a value between 8.4 and 9.9 with non-zero digits given for thousandths and below.
		
		or
		
		Indicates a value as a number between 840000 and 1000000 with non-zero digits given for hundreds and below
		eg
		• '9.167×10^5'
		• '8.415×10^5'
		• '916666.6667'
		• '916700'
			For 2m accept a response not given in standard form where the equivalent answer in digits would have no non-zero digits for hundreds and below
			eg
			    0.917×10^6
			
			For 1m accept a response not given in standard form where the equivalent answer in digits would have non-zero digits for hundreds and below
			eg
			    0.9167×10^6
			
			For 1m accept a response using the E notation with a value between 8.4 and 9.9 inclusive
			eg
			    9.16667 E + 5
			or
			Accept a response involving a value between 8.4 and 9.9 inclusive with $(+)5$ or $(+)05$
			eg
			    9.16667 05

Marks		Correct response	Additional guidance

| | 24 | | **Storm** (cont) |
| 2m | c | **For 2m** indicates a value between 7.9 and 8.7 inclusive
eg
• '8'
• '8$\frac{1}{3}$'

For only 1m shows in working a correct computation for distance, or a correct computation relating to the distance travelled by sound in 1 second
eg
• '$\frac{1200}{3600} \times 25$'
• '$\frac{1.2 \times 10^3}{60 \times 60} \times 25$'
• '$1.2 \times 10^3 \div 3600$'
• '$1200 \div 60 \div 60$'
• '$20 \div 60$' | |

Printed in the United Kingdom for The Stationery Office
J34778 2/98 8M 9385 7556